Metals Powders

Metals Powders

Synthesis and Processing

Special Issue Editor

Francisco P. Gómez Cuevas

MDPI • Basel • Beijing • Wuhan • Barcelona • Belgrade • Manchester • Tokyo • Cluj • Tianjin

Special Issue Editor
Francisco P. Gómez Cuevas
University of Huelva
Spain

Editorial Office
MDPI
St. Alban-Anlage 66
4052 Basel, Switzerland

This is a reprint of articles from the Special Issue published online in the open access journal *Metals* (ISSN 2075-4701) (available at: https://www.mdpi.com/journal/metals/special_issues/metals_powders).

For citation purposes, cite each article independently as indicated on the article page online and as indicated below:

LastName, A.A.; LastName, B.B.; LastName, C.C. Article Title. *Journal Name* **Year**, *Article Number*, Page Range.

ISBN 978-3-03936-062-8 (Pbk)
ISBN 978-3-03936-063-5 (PDF)

Cover image courtesy of Francisco Paula Gómez Cuevas.

Contents

About the Special Issue Editor

Francisco G. Cuevas, Dr. Industrial Engineer, obtained his title at the University of Seville (Spain), actually senior lecturer of Materials Science and Metallurgical Engineering at the University of Huelva, Spain. He has authored about 80 scientific publications covering different topics, such as powder metallurgy processing of Al alloys, the study of effective properties in porous materials, modelling and simulation of field assisted sintering processes, and the experimentation with these techniques. Present new research fields are the study of amorphisation processes and the subsequent consolidation of these materials via electrical sintering processes. The thread running through his scientific activity is the study of the relations between the processing parameters and the final microstructure of metals.

Editorial

Metals Powders: Synthesis and Processing

Francisco Paula Gómez Cuevas

Department of Chemical Engineering, Physical Chemistry and Materials Science, Escuela Técnica Superior de Ingeniería, Universidad de Huelva, Campus El Carmen, Avda. Tres de marzo s/n, 21071 Huelva, Spain; fgcuevas@dqcm.uhu.es

Received: 12 December 2019; Accepted: 15 December 2019; Published: 17 December 2019

1. Introduction and Scope

Metallic parts can be obtained by a wide variety of techniques. One of these techniques, traditionally known as powder metallurgy, uses powders as starting materials, which must be processed to obtain the final products. The European annual production and use of metal powders can alone be estimated to be more than one million tonnes. Powder synthesis through mechanical alloying, atomization, evaporation–condensation, electrochemical reduction processes, phase separation, etc., leads to a wide range of purities, alloys compositions, particle sizes and shapes, and microstructures; some of these properties are only possible to achieve through the techniques used for powders production. The demand for advanced material compositions and microstructures in transportation, aeronautics, medicine, energy production and several other fields, makes the use of metal powders an interesting technique for the production of metallic pieces. The extensive variety of metal powders, not only regarding compositions but also microstructures, makes the production and use of powders a continuously increasing market.

These powders can then be processed through traditional powder metallurgy cold-press and sinter techniques, hot isostatic pressing, injection moulding, field-assisted electrical sintering techniques or additive manufacturing techniques, among others. Under appropriate processing conditions, these techniques lead to materials with tailored properties that would be impossible to attain with other procedures. Near net shape components, with complex shapes and good dimensional precision make further processes unnecessary.

In this frame, this Book of Metals covers research works on recent advancements in some of the techniques used for the synthesis and processing of metals powders.

2. Contributions

The Book gathers works from academic researchers with new results. It consists of ten research papers focused on different materials and processes. The studied materials cover pure Ti [1,2] and Ta [3], and alloys with compositions Fe-Co-Cu [4], Al-Ti [5], Al-Mg-Si [6], Co-Cr-W-V [7], Mn-Bi [8], Fe-Si-B [9] and Fe-WC [10].

Some of these paper focus on the synthesis of metallic powders. Thus, Hwang at al. [3] studied the extraction of Ta powder, and Choi et al. [2] the extraction of Ti. Ball milling is the technique used by Xiang et al. [8] to obtain Mn-Bi powders with outstanding magnetic properties. Other manuscripts deal with the processing of metallic powders. Guerra et al. [4] studied the sintering of Fe-Co-Cu powder mixtures for their use as diamond impregnated tools for cutting granite stones. Urban et al. [5] studied the consolidation by electrical resistance sintering of mechanically alloyed amorphous Al-Ti powders. Magnetic properties are studied by Sun et al. [9] in cold pressed Fe-Si-B alloys. Kim et al. [6] studied the fabrication of functionally graded Al-based materials by hot extrusion. Civantos et al. [1] processed Ti by the space holder technique to be used as medical implants. Hard Co-based material processed by sintering was studied by Niannian et al. [7], and Fe-WC hardmetals processed by electrical resistance sintering by Cintas et al. [10].

Manuscripts can also be grouped according to the microstructure of the studied powders. Several manuscripts [1–4,6,10] deal with crystalline materials, whereas other works [5,7–9] use amorphous powders. According to the country of the corresponding author, three papers come from China [7–9], another three from Korea [2,3,6], two from Spain [5,10], one from USA-Spain [1], and one from Portugal [4]. In addition, authors from the United Kingdom, Germany, Mexico and Romania have contributed to the different papers.

Regarding powders synthesis, the production of Ti from TiO_2 by self-propagating high-temperature synthesis using Mg powder as reducing agent is studied in [2]. This process, avoiding the use of $TiCl_4$, produces magnesium and magnesium oxide by-products that need being removed. Different HCl acid leaching conditions are studied, finally obtaining a total oxygen content of the Ti powder of about 1 wt.%. On the other hand, Ta is obtained via reduction of tantalum pentoxide (Ta_2O_5) with Mg gas [3]. The powder obtained again contains MgO, also dissolved and removed in a water-based HCl solution. The final oxygen content was this time about 1.3 wt.%.

The production of Mn-Bi alloyed powders is studied in [8]. These are promising rare-earth-free permanent magnetic materials. The selected way to avoid Mn segregation in low-temperature phase MnBi is through melt spinning. Ribbons are annealed and then transformed into powders both with and without surfactant assisted ball milling processes. Surfactant assisted milled Mn_{55}-Bi_{45} powders have a higher size reduction during milling, but higher decomposition of low-temperature MnBi phase and lower saturation magnetization. Powders milled without surfactant show improved coercivity (18.2 kOe at room temperature and 23.5 kOe at 380 K), and in general better magnetic properties.

Powders processing studies include a wider range of techniques. The simpler technique consisted in pressing Fe-Si-B amorphous powders to prepare amorphous magnetic powder cores [9]. Particle size distribution, moulding pressure, and coating agent content were studied, with better results for intermediate particles size, moulding pressure about 2.40 GPa and addition of 1.5 wt.% sodium silicate.

The traditional powder metallurgy technique of press and sinter is used in [4] in the form of hot pressing to produce Fe-Co-Cu discs, which after adding 2.5 wt.% of diamond pieces, are used to cut granite stones. The composition 72wt.% Fe–25wt.% Co–3 wt.% Cu showed the best results in terms of toughness, diamond retention capacity and lower wear rate. Hot press sintering is also used in [7] to prepare a hard and tough Co-based alloy. Powders of Co, C, W, Ni, V and C were mechanically alloyed up to reach the amorphous state. After consolidation, the Co matrix and different carbides allow reaching hardness of 960 HV and fracture toughness of 10.5 MPa·m$^{1/2}$.

This same traditional PM technique is used in [1] to produce Ti implants. However, the use of 50 vol % NH_4HCO_3 space-holder allows producing porous samples resembling the bones structure. Produced materials achieved suitable cell biocompatibility, with the best mechanical behaviour to replace cortical bone tissues when fabricated with 100–200 µm space-holders.

Hot extrusion process is studied in [6] to fabricate functionally graded Al-base materials. Functionally graded materials improve the interfaces to prevent cracks coming from residual stresses in a heterogeneous material. Experiments to improve the interfacial properties were carried out by using Al3003 powder and bulk Al6063 alloys. After extruding at 468 °C with a ratio of 100, the interface between the two materials showed almost no cracks, resulting a final product with high strength and adequate elongation.

A different sintering technique, electrical resistance sintering, is used in [5] with previously mechanically alloyed amorphous Al-Ti powders. This work studies the possibility of retaining such unstable structure after sintering with a very quick process. The amorphous structure is at least partially retained after sintering for 1.2 s, attaining a remarkable final hardness in the sintered compacts. In addition, electrical resistance sintering is used in [10] to produce WC-6 wt.% Co hardmetals. The initial powders with WC particle size of about 260 nm are processed by a sintering process lasting about 2 s, resulting hardness values higher than 1900 HV, and maintaining the ultrafine WC grain size in the order of the 300 nm, all without the need for using a protective atmosphere.

Thus, this book includes interdisciplinary research works that address different synthesis and processing techniques applied to metal powders. I hope this small compendium of works among the vast options for powder synthesis and processing serves the researcher starting in the powders world, providing a vision of the different possible techniques, and enables those working for a long time in this area to stimulate future scientific ideas and works.

Acknowledgments: As Guest Editor, I would like to thank Cheryl Huo, Assistant Editor, for her support and active role in the publication. Also the entire staff of Metals Editorial Office is grateful for the precious collaboration. Furthermore, I am also thankful to all of the contributing authors and reviewers; without their excellent work it would not have been possible to complete this Special Issue and Book that hopefully will serve to researchers as reference literature.

Conflicts of Interest: The authors declare no conflict of interest.

References

1. Civantos, A.; Beltrán, A.M.; Domínguez-Trujillo, C.; Garvi, M.D.; Lebrato, J.; Rodríguez-Ortiz, J.A.; García-Moreno, F.; Cauich-Rodriguez, J.V.; Guzman, J.J.; Torres, Y. Balancing porosity and mechanical properties of titanium samples to favor cellular growth against bacteria. *Metals* **2019**, *9*, 1039. [CrossRef]
2. Choi, S.H.; Sim, J.J.; Lim, J.H.; Seo, S.J.; Kim, D.W.; Hyun, S.K.; Park, K.T. Removal of Mg and MgO by-products through magnesiothermic reduction of Ti powder in self-propagating high-temperature synthesis. *Metals* **2019**, *9*, 169. [CrossRef]
3. Hwang, S.M.; Wang, J.P.; Lee, D.W. Extraction of Tantalum powder via the magnesium reduction of tantalum pentoxide. *Metals* **2019**, *9*, 205. [CrossRef]
4. Guerra Rosa, L.; Anjinho, C.A.; Amaral, P.M.; Cruz Fernandes, J. Mechanical properties of some metallic powder alloys and their contribution to the performance of diamond tools used for cutting granite. *Metals* **2019**, *9*, 1219. [CrossRef]
5. Urban, P.; Ternero, F.; Caballero, E.S.; Nandyala, S.; Montes, J.M.; Cuevas, F.G. Amorphous Al-Ti Powders prepared by mechanical alloying and consolidated by electrical resistance sintering. *Metals* **2019**, *9*, 1140. [CrossRef]
6. Kim, D.; Park, K.; Chang, M.; Joo, S.; Hong, S.; Cho, S.; Kwon, H. Fabrication of functionally graded materials using aluminum alloys via hot extrusion. *Metals* **2019**, *9*, 210. [CrossRef]
7. Li, N.; Yin, F.; Feng, L. Microstructure of a V-containing cobalt based alloy prepared by mechanical alloying and hot pressed sintering. *Metals* **2019**, *9*, 464. [CrossRef]
8. Li, X.; Pan, D.; Xiang, Z.; Lu, W.; Batalu, D. Microstructure and magnetic properties of Mn55Bi45 powders obtained by different ball milling processes. *Metals* **2019**, *9*, 441. [CrossRef]
9. Sun, H.; Wang, C.; Chen, W.; Lin, J. Strategy to enhance magnetic properties of Fe78Si9B13 amorphous powder cores in the industrial condition. *Metals* **2019**, *9*, 381. [CrossRef]
10. Cintas, J.; Astacio, R.; Cuevas, F.G.; Montes, J.M.; Weissgaerber, T.; Lagos, M.A.; Torres, Y.; Gallardo, J.M. Production of ultrafine grained hardmetals by electrical resistance sintering. *Metals* **2019**, *9*, 159. [CrossRef]

Article

Extraction of Tantalum Powder via the Magnesium Reduction of Tantalum Pentoxide

Seon-Min Hwang [1], Jei-Pil Wang [2,*] and Dong-Won Lee [1,*]

[1] Titanium Department, Korea Institute of Materials Science (KIMS), Changwon, Gyeongnam 641-010, Korea; seonmin@kims.re.kr

[2] Department of Metallurgical Engineering, Pukyoung National University, Busan 48513, Korea

*   Correspondence: ldw1623@kims.re.kr (D.-W.L.); jpwang@pknu.ac.kr (J.-P.W.);
    Tel.: +82-55-280-3524 (D.-W.L.); +82-51-629-6341 (J.-P.W.)

Received: 22 December 2018; Accepted: 4 February 2019; Published: 9 February 2019

Abstract: The metallic tantalum powder was successfully synthesized via reduction of tantalum pentoxide (Ta_2O_5) with magnesium gas at 1073~1223 K for 10 h inside the chamber held under an argon atmosphere. The powder obtained after reduction shows the Ta–MgO mixed structure and that the MgO component was dissolved and removed fully via stirring in a water-based HCl solution. The particle size in the tantalum powder obtained after acid leaching was shown to be in a range of 50~300 nm, and the mean internal crystallite sizes measured by the Scherrer equation varied from 11.5 to 24.7 nm according to the increase in reduction temperatures. The temperature satisfactory for a maximal reduction effect was found to be 1173 K because the oxygen content was minimally saturated to about 1.3 wt %.

Keywords: tantalum powder; magnesium reduction; Ta_2O_5 powder; MgO; HCl solution

1. Introduction

Tantalum is one of the key rare metals that has an extremely high melting temperature of 3290 K. Due to the excellent elasticity and corrosion resistance, it has been actively used as an alloying element into a super-alloy applied in the military parts such as jet engine, missile, and so on [1–3]. Additionally, the dielectric properties of the anodic oxide have allowed for its application as a raw material in the production of capacitors in the electronic industry [4]. Therefore, many studies have been done to secure high-purity tantalum material.

Generally, pure metals are extracted via reduction of their oxide phase with a reductant media such as hydrogen or carbon [5]. In the case of tantalum metal, tantalum pentoxide (Ta_2O_5) has been regarded as an initial material, but its reduction is nearly impossible, practically and theoretically, by hydrogen gas, by vacuum, or by carbon due to its high thermodynamic stability.

Conventionally, metallic tantalum powder is produced via reaction of tantalum pentoxide (Ta_2O_5) as a raw material, hydrofluoric acid (HF) and potassium fluoride (KF) as catalysts, and sodium as a reductant [6]. However, it has been considered that such reducing agents are considerably harmful. Several works have been found in fields using special reducers such as aluminum, magnesium, and silicon [7–10]. Among them, calcium is risky at an enhanced temperature. Applying aluminum has made it difficult to remove the aluminum oxide formed after reduction. Molten aluminum or calcium is usually used as a reductant [11]. When using magnesium, we found that 1) the reduction temperature is relatively low, 2) handling is relatively easier, and 3), after reduction via magnesium, the magnesium oxide (MgO) of a by-product can be easily eliminated by acid leaching. On the other hand, the main drawback in magnesiothermic reduction is the considerable consumption of magnesium by vaporization; moreover, the precise and careful removal of fine metallic magnesium particles condensed on the surface of the inner reactor is required. To avoid such difficulty, self-propagating high-temperature synthesis (SHS) has been studied with preform compacted with magnesium powder [12–14]. In spite of the above-mentioned drawbacks, many works on magnesiothermic gas reduction from tantalum oxide to tantalum have been done. However, multiple oxides, such as $MgTa_2O_6$ and $Mg_4Ta_2O_9$, have been employed as raw materials to produce nanosized tantalum powder [15,16]. Scrap recycling, the flux effect, and so on have been studied with fixed reduction temperatures [8,17,18]. In this study, we investigated the reduction behavior from pure tantalum oxide to tantalum powder via magnesium gas with various reduction temperatures and studied the characterizations of product powders, such as the phase evaluation and microstructure.

2. Experiment Methods

For the magnesium reduction, we used tantalum pentoxide powder (99.99%) and pure magnesium (99.9%) purchased from Jiujiang Ltd. (Jiujiang, China) as raw materials. The reactors for the reduction were made of stainless steel, and the framework of the reactor inside for inserting raw material and magnesium is represented in Figure 1. Twenty grams of tantalum oxide powder was inserted, and the amount of magnesium needed to reduce it fully was 5.4 g theoretically. However, because magnesium not only reacts with Ta_2O_5 but can also be consumed by condensation on the surface of the inner wall of the upper reactor, 10 g of excess magnesium was prepared.

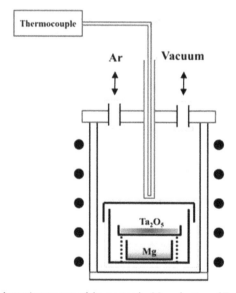

Figure 1. Schematic structure of the reactor for Mg reduction of Ta_2O_5 powder.

After repetitively treating the reactor with a vacuum and argon gas atmosphere and filling it to 1.5 atm of argon gas, it was heated at a rate of 10 K/min to 1073 K, 1123 K, 1173 K, and 1223 K for reduction reactions, respectively. The reduction time was fixed to 10 h, and the argon atmosphere was held for a full period until it was cooled to room temperature. The reduction reaction took place with magnesium gas that was evaporated from liquefied magnesium and tantalum oxide. The magnesium oxide formed after the reduction was removed by chemical washing with stirring and a filtering technique in a 5% hydrochloric acid solution. Tantalum metal powders were then obtained. We characterized the microstructure, phase evaluation, and chemical compositions with a scanning electron microscope (MIRA3 LM) (TESCAN, Brno, Czech Republic), an X-ray diffractometer (D/Max 2500) (Rigaku, Tokyo, Japan), and an oxygen–nitrogen analyzer (ELTRA ON-900) (ELTRA, Haan, Germany).

3. Result and Discussion

The reduction occurred in the reaction via magnesium gas and tantalum oxide, and resulted in the formation of a secondary product, magnesium oxide, inside which reduced metallic tantalum powder may have existed. The reason why this reaction is possible can be explained by the fact that the thermodynamic stability of magnesium oxide is much higher than that of tantalum oxide.

Figure 2 is the SEM microstructure of the raw material powder and the tantalum pentoxide, whose overall-round shape shows an agglomerated morphology. Its size was in the range of about 200–500 nm. X-ray diffraction was studied for phase evaluation, and the result is represented in Figure 3.

Figure 2. SEM microstructure of raw Ta_2O_5 powder.

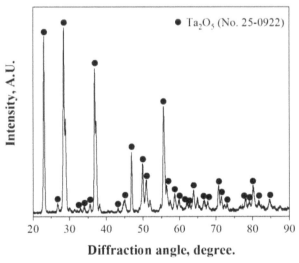

Figure 3. X-ray diffraction patterns measured in the raw Ta_2O_5 powder.

The equilibrium phase diagram of magnesium and tantalum in Figure 4 was studied using thermochemical software (FactSage 7.2, collaborative between THERMFACT/CRCT (Montreal, QC, Canada) and GTT-Technologies (Aachen, Germany) [19]. We found no mutual solubility between magnesium gas and metal tantalum in the region of temperature reduction. Therefore, the magnesium gas, a reducing agent, only reduced the oxygen component in the tantalum oxide and did not alloy with metal tantalum. Therefore, because it is possible to remove only the components of the formed magnesium oxide and the unreacted magnesium mixed with the product, metallic tantalum powder could be effectively obtained.

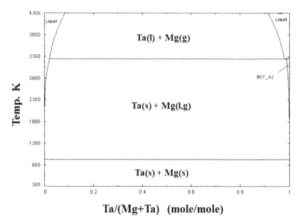

Figure 4. Ta–Mg phase diagram.

As shown in Equation (1) below, the change in the free energy obtained by HSC-5.1 software about magnesium reduction reaction in the area of 1073~1223 K is about –900 kJ/mole, which shows that the driving force for reaction is tremendous.

$$Ta_2O_5(s) + 5Mg(g) = 2Ta(s) + 5MgO(s) \quad \Delta G_{1073\,K \sim 1223\,K} = -987 \sim -891 \text{ kJ/mole} \quad (1)$$

The reduction behavior can be explained by the relation of the diffusion pass of oxygen. That is, as shown in Figure 5, the Mg reduction of tantalum oxide started from the powder surface via magnesium gas and led to the formation of a film of magnesium oxide. By a continuous reaction with magnesium gas existing outside, the oxygen component inside the particles was diffused out in the direction of $Ta_2O_5 \rightarrow Ta_2O \rightarrow Ta$ while the reduction reaction was processed. The reason why the reduction was processed with the formation of Ta_2O is based on the confirmation of the existence of an insufficiently reduced phase, Ta_2O, as shown in Figure 10.

After the reduction reaction was finished, metal tantalum powder may have existed inside the powder and the magnesium oxide formed on the surface. Since the formed magnesium oxide components can be fully removed via agitating and washing in weak hydrochloric acid, pure metal tantalum powders were gained. The changes in Gibbs free energy of the reaction where magnesium oxide was washed and removed in a hydrochloric acid solution can be expressed in the following equations:

$$Mg + 2HCl = MgCl_2 + H_2 \quad \Delta G_{298K} = -401 \text{ kJ/mole} \quad (2)$$

$$MgO + 2HCl = MgCl_2 + H_2O \quad \Delta G_{298K} = -61 \text{ kJ/mole} \quad (3)$$

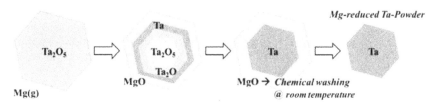

Figure 5. Schematic concept of the reduction behavior from Ta_2O_5 to Ta via magnesium gas.

Figures 6 and 7 represent the X-ray diffraction profile and SEM microstructure studied in the powder reduced at 1173 K, that is, before removing the magnesium oxide. The two phases of tantalum and magnesium oxide without tantalum oxides shown in Figure 6 indicate that the reduction reaction was well processed.

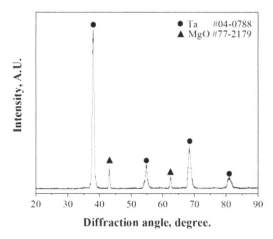

Figure 6. X-ray diffraction patterns measured in the Mg-reduced sample at 1173 K before acid leaching.

In the SEM microstructure (Figure 7), the particles are hundreds of nanometers in size and appear to be in an absorbed state by small particles with dozens of nanometers. These absorbed particles were estimated to be particles of magnesium oxide formed by the reduction, and this formation is found in reduction process.

Figure 7. SEM microstructure of the Mg-reduced powder at 1173 K before acid leaching.

Figure 8 is the SEM microstructures of the pure tantalum powder obtained after reduction at 1073 K and 1173 K after acid leaching. Overall, the particles have a finer morphology than those of the raw material shown in Figure 2, particularly if the sample is at less than 1073 K. The formation of such fine structures can be explained by the restraint effect of the growth of tantalum nuclei because the reduction temperature is much lower than the melting point of tantalum metal.

Figure 8. SEM microstructure of the Mg-reduced sample at (**a**) 1073 K and (**b**) 1173 K after acid leaching.

There is a possibility that the relatively coarse particles shown in Figure 8 are poly-crystallite and are not single-crystallite. Therefore, we measured the size of the internal crystallites by using the Scherrer equation ($B = K\lambda/D \cdot \cos\theta_B$) [20], and the result is shown in Figure 9.

The Scherrer equation was applied to the 1st peak in the XRD profiles. B is the full width at half maximum, HWHM (radian) is the diffraction peak, λ is the wavelength of the radiation (nm), θ_B is the Bragg angle, and D is the crystallite size (nm), respectively. Figure 9 indicates that the average crystalline sizes were increased within a range of 11.5~24.7 nm according to an increase in reduction temperatures, and this was considered to be a crystal growth effect.

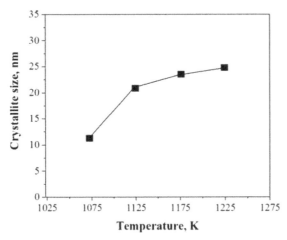

Figure 9. Crystallite sizes obtained by the Scherrer method in Mg-reduced tantalum powder.

In the next step, we compared all X-ray profiles diffracted in powders produced at various reduction temperatures, and this result is shown in Figure 10. The insufficiently reduced phase, Ta_2O, shown in Figure 5 was shown in the samples at relatively low reduction temperatures. Temperatures over 1173 K indicated a clear tantalum peak. Such insufficient reductions at lower temperatures resulted from the effect of a lower reduction driving force and the partial pressure of magnesium gas.

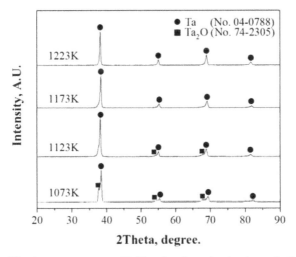

Figure 10. X-ray diffraction patterns measured in Mg-reduced samples at various reduction temperatures.

The oxygen content of the tantalum metal powder obtained from each reduction was analyzed quantitatively (Table 1). The oxygen content of the reduced powder at 1073 K was very high, 11.57 wt %, and decreased gradually to 1.25 wt % with the increase in reduction temperature. The oxygen content in the tantalum powder may have originated from inner oxygen components in the tantalum particles and the passive film formed on the surface. Therefore, the oxygen in the samples at 1173 K and 1223 K, where the reductions were well formed, was mainly detected in the passive surface film. On the contrary, in the samples insufficiently reduced at 1073 K and 1123 K, the oxygen may have come from both inside the powder and from the passive film. However, we insist the oxygen came from the passive film because the particles produced at low temperature were significantly fine (Figure 8a), which caused high specific surface areas (Table 1). Turning to the samples at 1173 K and 1223 K, it was shown that the detected oxygen content was not much different. We concluded that the reduction temperature of 1173 K is a more satisfactory condition in view of thermal energy saving.

Table 1. Oxygen content (wt %) and specific surface area (m^2/g) measured in Mg-reduced tantalum powder at different temperatures.

Temp., K	1073	1123	1173	1223
O, wt %	11.57	6.46	1.35	1.25
S, m^2/g	21.81	12.23	7.11	6.52

4. Conclusion

Pure tantalum powder was successfully produced via magnesium reduction with tantalum pentoxide as a raw material. The structure of the powder after Mg reduction was in an agglomerated form of tiny particles of dozens of nm absorbed on the surface of coarse particles. After removing the magnesium oxide component in a hydrochloric acid solution, tantalum powder was transfigured to a structure with a range of particle sizes, approximately 50~300 nm, finer than the particle sizes of raw powder. The reduction reaction occurred via Ta_2O in an intermediate phase.

As a result of X-ray analysis in tantalum metal powders obtained by various reduction temperatures, full reduction occurred at over 1173 K. The oxygen content of the produced powder was shown then to be in a minimal range of 1.25~1.35 wt %. The average crystalline size in powders, determined by the Scherrer equation, increased from 11.5 to 24.7 nm with the increase in reduction temperature.

Author Contributions: Writing—original draft preparation, S.M.H. and D.W.L.; writing—review and editing, J.P.W.

Funding: This research received no external funding.

Conflicts of Interest: The authors declare no conflict of interest.

References

1. Cardonne, S.M.; Kumar, P.; Michaluk, C.A.; Schwartz, H.D. Tantalum and its Alloys. *Int. J. Refract. Met. Hard Mater.* **1995**, *13*, 187–191. [CrossRef]
2. Won, H.I.; Nersisyan, H.H.; Won, C.W. Combustion synthesis-derived tantalum powder for solid-electrolyte capacitor. *J. Alloys Compd.* **2009**, *478*, 716–720. [CrossRef]
3. Han, F.F.; Chang, J.X.; Li, H.; Lou, L.H.; Zhang, J. Influence of Ta content on hot corrosion behavior of a directionally solidified nickel base superalloy. *J. Alloys Compd.* **2015**, *619*, 102–108. [CrossRef]
4. Korinek, G.J. Tantalum in Solid Electrolytic Capacitors-New Developments. *Mater. Trans.* **1996**, *37*, 1244–1246. [CrossRef]
5. Loveleen, B.K.; Gourav, S.; Navjot, K.; Pandey, O.P. Thermal stability and structural properties of Ta nanopowder synthesized via simultaneous reduction of Ta_2O_5 by hydrogen and carbon. *J. Therm. Anal. Calorim.* **2015**, *119*, 175–182.
6. Kolosov, V.N.; Orlov, V.M.; Miroshnichenko, M.N.; Prokhorova, T.Yu. Preparation of Tantalum Powders via the Sodium Reduction of Potassium Heptafluorotantalate Heat-Treated in Air. *Inorg. Mater.* **2015**, *51*, 116–121. [CrossRef]
7. Brito, R.A. de.; Medeiros, F.F.P.; Gomes, U.U.; Costa, F.A.; Silva, A.G.P.; Alves Jr, C. Production of tantalum by aluminothermic reduction in plasma reactor. *Refract. Met. Hard Mater.* **2008**, *26*, 433–437. [CrossRef]
8. Okabe, T.H.; Sato, N.; Mitsuda, Y.; Ono, S. Production of Tantalum Powder by Magnesiothermic Reduction of Feed Preform. *Mater. Trans.* **2003**, *44*, 2646–2653. [CrossRef]
9. Awasthi, A.; Bhatt, Y.J.; Krishnamurthy, N.; Ueda, Y.; Garg, S.P. The reduction of niobium and tantalum pentoxides by silicon in vacuum. *J. Alloys Compd.* **2001**, *315*, 187–192. [CrossRef]

10. Purushotham, Y.; Ravindranath, K.; Kumar, A.; Govindaiah, R.; Prakash, T.L. Quality improvements in tantalum powder by automation of sodium. *Inter. J. Refract. Met. Hard Mater.* **2009**, *27*, 571–576.
11. Munter, R.; Parshin, A.; Yamshchikov, L.; Plotnikov, V.; Gorkunov, V.; Kober, V. Reduction of tantalum pentoxide with aluminium and calcium: Thermodynamic modeling and scale skilled test. *Proc. Est. Acad. Sci.* **2010**, *59*, 243–252. [CrossRef]
12. Nersisyan, H.H.; Lee, J.H.; Lee, S.I.; Won, C.W. The role of the reaction medium in the self propagating high temperature synthesis of nanosized tantalum powder. *Combust. Flame.* **2003**, *135*, 539–545. [CrossRef]
13. Orlov, V.M.; Kryzhanov, M.V. Magnesium-Thermic Reduction of Tantalum Oxide by Self-propagating High-Temperature Synthesis. *Russ. Metall.* **2010**, *2010*, 384–388. [CrossRef]
14. Orlov, V.M.; Kryzhanov, M.V. Deoxidation of the Tantalum Powder Produced by Self-Propagating High-Temperature Synthesis. *Russ. Metall.* **2014**, *2014*, 191–194. [CrossRef]
15. Orlov, V.M.; Kryzhanov, M.V. Production of Tantalum Powders by the Magnesium Reduction of Tantalates. *Russ. Metall.* **2015**, *2015*, 590–593. [CrossRef]
16. Orlov, V.M.; Kryzhanov, M.V.; Kalinnikov, V.T. Magnesium Reduction of Tantalum Oxide Compounds. *Dokl. Chem.* **2014**, *457*, 160–163. [CrossRef]
17. Mineta, K.; Okabe, T.H. Development of a recycling process for tantalum from capacitor scraps. *J. Phys. Chem. Solids.* **2005**, *66*, 318–321. [CrossRef]
18. Muller, R.; Bobeth, M.; Brumm, H.; Gille, G.; Pompe, W.; Thomas, J. Kinetics of nanoscale structure development during Mg-vapour reduction of tantalum oxide. *Int. J. Mater. Res.* **2007**, *98*, 1138–1145. [CrossRef]
19. Collection of Phase Diagrams. Available online: http://www.crct.polymtl.ca/fact/phase_diagram.php?file=Mg-Ta.jpg&dir=FTlite (accessed on 9 February 2019).
20. Miranda, M.A.R.; Sasaki, J.M. The limit of application of the Scherrer equation. *Acta Crystallogr. Sect. A* **2018**, *74*, 54–65. [CrossRef] [PubMed]

Article

Removal of Mg and MgO By-Products through Magnesiothermic Reduction of Ti Powder in Self-Propagating High-Temperature Synthesis

Sang Hoon Choi [1,2], Jae Jin Sim [1], Jae Hong Lim [1,2], Seok-Jun Seo [1], Dong-Wook Kim [3], Soong-Keun Hyun [2] and Kyoung-Tae Park [1,*]

[1] Korea Institute for Rare Metals, Korea Institute of Industrial Technology, Incheon 21999, Korea; csh33@kitech.re.kr (S.H.C.); simjae@kitech.re.kr (J.J.S.); cow1boy@kitech.re.kr (J.H.L.); sjseo@kitech.re.kr (S.-J.S.)
[2] Department of Advanced Materials Engineering, In-Ha University, Incheon 22212, Korea; skhyun@inha.ac.kr
[3] Department of Chemical Engineering, In-Ha University, Incheon 22212, Korea; dwkim86@inha.ac.kr
* Correspondence: ktpark@kitech.re.kr; Tel.: +82-32-458-5199

Received: 2 January 2019; Accepted: 29 January 2019; Published: 1 February 2019

Abstract: Commercial production of titanium involves chlorination using chlorine gas that can be converted to hydrochloric acid by atmospheric moisture and is hazardous to human health. In the titanium production process, self-propagating high-temperature synthesis is one of the process to directly reduce titanium dioxide. In this work, titanium powder was prepared by self-propagating high-temperature synthesis using titanium dioxide as the starting material and magnesium powder as a reducing agent. After the reaction, magnesium and magnesium oxide by-products were then removed by acid leaching under different leaching conditions, leaving behind pure Ti. During each leaching condition, the temperature of the leaching solution was carefully monitored. After leaching, the recovered titanium in the form of a powder was collected, washed with water and dried in a vacuum oven. Detailed compositional, structural, and morphological analyses were performed to determine the presence of residual reaction by-products. It was found that leaching in 0.4 M hydrochloric acid followed by second leaching in 7.5 M hydrochloric acid is the optimum leaching condition. Furthermore, it was also noticed that total volume of solution in 0.4 M hydrochloric acid leaching condition is advantageous to maintain uniform temperature during the process.

Keywords: titanium powder; self-propagating high-temperature synthesis; acid leaching; magnesium; magnesium oxide

---

1. Introduction

Titanium (Ti) is commonly used in the aerospace, chemical, petrochemical, maritime, and biomedical fields due to its outstanding properties, including low density, high corrosion resistance, high specific strength, and biocompatibility [1,2]. Commercially, titanium is produced using the Kroll process, which is based on the magnesiothermic reduction of titanium tetrachloride ($TiCl_4$) [2,3]. While the Kroll process can produce high-quality titanium, it is a batch-type process and is therefore costly, has a low productivity, and presents an environmental hazard because of the release of chlorine gas [4]. For these reasons, researchers have been attempting to replace the Kroll process with new titanium production processes such as the Fray Farthing Chen (FFC) Cambridge process [5], Ono and Suzuki (OS) process [6], preform reduction process (PRP) [7], Armstrong process [8,9], and hydrogen-assisted magnesiothermic reduction (HAMR) process [10].

Titanium dioxide (TiO_2) is used as a raw material in the FFC, OS, PRP, and HAMR processes, while $TiCl_4$ is used in the Kroll and Armstrong processes. TiO_2 is safer to handle and easier to transport than $TiCl_4$, which is a highly toxic chemical. Therefore, when using TiO_2, it is less important for the Ti metal production plant and raw material production plant to be in close proximity to each other [10]. In addition, in the 1990s, it was reported that $TiCl_4$ is one of the most dangerous water-reactive substances because hydrogen chloride gas forms when liquid $TiCl_4$ reacts with atmospheric moisture [11]. However, TiO_2 is much more difficult to reduce than $TiCl_4$ because the Ti-O and Ti-Ti bonding energies have a high chemical affinity for oxygen at 2.12 eV and 2.56 eV, respectively [10,12].

In the processes described above, magnesium (Mg) and calcium (Ca) are used as reducing agents. Oxides such as MgO and CaO, as well as residual Mg and Ca, are present as by-products and must be removed by leaching. For example, in the PRP process, Ca vapors are used as the reducing agent. In the leaching process, acetic acid (CH_3COOH), and hydrochloric acid (HCl) are used as the leaching solution to remove the by-products [7]. Mg is used as a reducing agent in the HAMR process, and hydrochloric acid is used as a leaching solution to remove residual Mg and MgO [10].

In our previous work, we produced Ti powder directly from Ti dioxide by self-propagating high-temperature synthesis (SHS) using Mg as a reducing agent. After leaching, a spherical Ti powder was prepared by plasma treatment. X-ray Diffraction (XRD) images of the sample produced by the SHS process are shown in Figure 1. MgO and residual Mg were detected as reaction by-products in addition to Ti [13]. No intermediate phases such as $Ti_{10}O_9$, Ti_3O_5, or Ti_2O_3 were identified. If these intermediate phases were to be produced, it would be almost impossible to achieve reduction using Mg as a reducing agent [14].

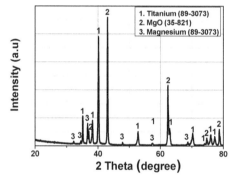

Figure 1. XRD analysis results of product of combustion synthesis of TiO_2 + 3Mg system [13].

From these points of view, SHS could be regarded as an alternative means of producing Ti metal since the process time and overall energy consumption of the SHS process are dramatically lower than those of a typical metallothermic reduction under isothermal heating conditions, given that the only energy input is that required to ignite the mixture of raw materials. In the present study, our purpose is the leaching of the products of SHS. We optimized selective leaching to remove Mg and MgO, thus leaving pure Ti powder. We have addressed the synthesis of Ti by the SHS process in a previous study [13]. Figure 1 shows the as-synthesized SHS products consisting of Ti, Mg, and MgO without any other Ti oxides, such as $Ti_{10}O_9$, Ti_3O_5, or Ti_2O_3.

2. Materials and Methods

2.1. Materials

Raw materials used in this study included: Ti powder was prepared by SHS using Titanium dioxide powder (TiO_2, 99.99 mass%, particle size 2 μm, Kojundo Chemical Laboratory Co., Ltd., Saitama, Japan) and Mg powder (Mg, >98.5 mass%, particle size <74 μm, DaeJung Chemicals and Metals Co., Ltd., Siheung, Korea) as raw materials. Acid solutions used in leaching to remove the Mg and MgO by-products were hydrochloric acid (HCl, 35–37 mass%, Junsei Chemical Co., Ltd., Tokyo, Japan) and acetic acid (CH$_3$COOH, 99.5 mass% min, OCI Co., Ltd., Seoul, Korea).

2.2. Methods

Leaching was performed using a hotplate with a k-type thermocouple installed to monitor the temperature of the solution during the leaching. The by-products, Mg and MgO, were removed with an acid solution, filtered, and then washed, as illustrated in Figure 2. The leaching experiments were classified into two groups, as shown in Table 1. Group 1 was subdivided into five experiments with different conditions; however, in each case, a single leaching process was used. The five experiments differed in the concentration of hydrochloric acid (HCl) used. Group 2 was subdivided into four experiments, all of which involved a two-step leaching process. Experiment 2–1 was first conducted using CH$_3$COOH, followed by HCl. All the other experiments except 2–1 were first conducted using a less-concentrated hydrochloric acid, followed by a strong HCl.

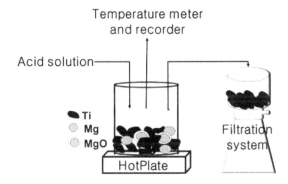

Figure 2. Leaching and filtration system for the removal of reaction by-products.

Table 1. Experimental acid leaching conditions for the removal of reaction by-products.

Group Number	Experiment Number	Step	Solvent	Concentration (M)	Amount of Product (g)	Total Volume of Solution (mL)	Stirring Time (h)	Stirring Speed (rpm)
Group 1	1–1			5				
	1–2			5.5				
	1–3	1	HCl	6.5		183	4	
	1–4			7				
	1–5			7.5				
Group 2	2–1	1	CH$_3$COOH	8.75		183	6	
		2	HCl	6.5	28	183	1	150
	2–2	1	HCl	0.6		183	6	
		2		6.5		183	1	
	2–3	1	HCl	0.6		183	6	
		2		7.5		183	1	
	2–4	1	HCl	0.4		3000	6	
		2		7.5		183	1	

Overall, 28 g of the SHS product was used, and the stirring speed was set as 150 rpm. After leaching, the sample was separated from the solution by filtration and then dried in a vacuum oven. After drying, the microstructure and crystallinity were determined by Field Emission-Scanning Electron Microscopy (FE-SEM, JEOL, JSM-7100F, Tokyo, Japan) and X-ray Diffraction (XRD, Bruker, D8 ADVANCE, Billerica, MA, USA with Cu-Kα radiation) analyses, while the oxygen content in the Ti powder was determined by Oxygen Nitrogen/Hydrogen analysis (ON/H, Eltra GmbH, ONH 2000, Haan, Germany).

3. Results and Discussion

Figure 3 shows the results of XRD analysis of the product at each experimental condition of group 1. In the XRD results, Ti was determined to be the main peak at the all experimental conditions of group 1. However, MgO was detected after leaching in all experimental condition, indicating that MgO was not completely removed. In addition, Mg(OH)$_2$ phase was formed under a low concentration of HCl condition, as can be seen in Figure 3a,b.

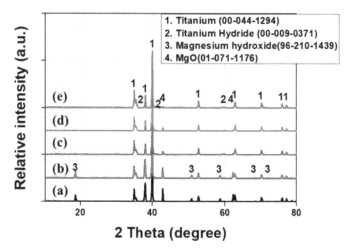

Figure 3. XRD profiles of samples obtained after leaching: (**a**) Experiment 1–1 (5 M HCl), (**b**) experiment 1–2 (5.5 M HCl), (**c**) experiment 1–3 (6.5 M HCl), (**d**) experiment 1–4 (7 M HCl), and (**e**) experiment 1–5 (7.5 M HCl).

To verify the presence of Mg(OH)$_2$, a Pourbaix diagram was drawn using the HSC Chemistry software (Chemistry Software, Houston, TX, USA) based on the pH and electrochemical potential of the Mg-H$_2$O system shown in Figure 4. The calculation conditions were set as 25, 50, 75, and 100 °C with a pH range of 0–14. The electrochemical potential range was set from −2 V to 2 V, relative to a standard hydrogen electrode (SHE) [15]. In the Pourbaix diagram obtained for Mg-H$_2$O, the inner part indicated by the dotted blue lines represents the stable region of H$_2$O. The area below the dotted blue lines is that in which the water is reduced and hydrogen is generated according to Equation (1). In the area above the dotted blue line, water is oxidized to generate oxygen, as defined by Equation (2).

$$2H^+ + 4e^- \rightarrow H_{2(g)} \tag{1}$$

$$2H_2O \rightarrow O_{2\,(g)} + 4H^+ + 4e \tag{2}$$

Figure 4 shows that, with an increase in the temperature from 25 °C to 100 °C, the stable region of Mg shrinks while that of the Mg(OH)$_2$ expands. Ideally, Mg(OH)$_2$ should not precipitate at pH < 8. However, as the temperature increases, Mg(OH)$_2$ can precipitate at pH < 8 at 50 °C and at pH < 7 at 100 °C.

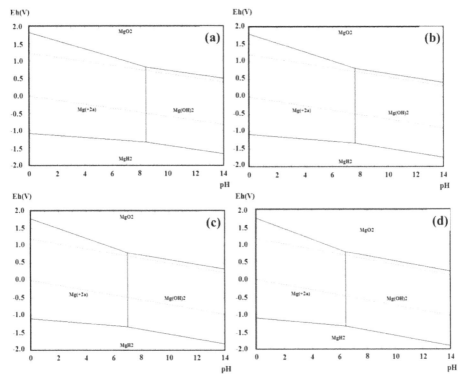

Figure 4. Pourbaix diagrams for Mg-H₂O system over a pH range of 0–14 and an electropotential range from −2.0 V to 2.0 V vs. SHE at (**a**) 25 °C, (**b**) 50 °C, (**c**) 75 °C, and (**d**) 100 °C.

The literature states that, at a lower pH, the ionizing strength of Mg^{2+} is stronger than the precipitating trace of $Mg(OH)_2$. On the other hand, at relatively higher temperatures, the amount of $Mg(OH)_2$ in the solution should gradually decrease [16]. The pH at which $Mg(OH)_2$ precipitates can be thermodynamically explained by Equations (3)–(5). The specific calculation procedure can be modified to calculate the pH using the Gibbs free energy Equation (3) and the equilibrium constant Equation (4). Using Equations (3) and (4), the pH of the solution was determined, as described in Equation (5). From Equation (5), the pH at which $Mg(OH)_2$ precipitates can be deduced from the concentration of Mg ions and the temperature of the solution system [17].

$$\Delta G^0 = -2.303RT \log_{10} K_T \tag{3}$$

where R is the ideal gas constant (8.314 J·K⁻¹·mol⁻¹), and T is the temperature as a function of the thermodynamic equilibrium quotient, K_T.

$$K_T = \frac{C_{products}}{C^0_{products}} \gamma_{products} / \frac{C_{reactants}}{C^0_{reactants}} \gamma_{reactants} \tag{4}$$

where γ is the activity coefficient, C is the concentration (mol·L⁻¹), and C^0 is the standard concentration of 1 mol·L⁻¹.

$$pH = \left(-\frac{\Delta G^0}{2.303RT} - \log_{10} \gamma_{Mg^{2+}} \left[Mg^{2+} \right] \right) / 2 \tag{5}$$

The detection of $Mg(OH)_2$ in experiments 1–1 and 1–2 can be explained by the occurrence of an exothermic reaction during acid leaching, caused by the contact between Mg, MgO, and HCl. It is also believed that $Mg(OH)_2$ precipitates as the pH increases due to ionization upon dissolution. $Mg(OH)_2$ precipitated only in experiments 1–1 and 1–2, and did not precipitate when a highly concentrated leaching solution was used.

The above phenomenon occurred because the pH of the leaching solution used to remove MgO and Mg was lower than that used for experiments 1–1 and 1–2. The pH can be expected to be lower than that at which $Mg(OH)_2$ precipitates, even when the pH increases during the leaching process. XRD analysis also confirmed the presence of TiH_2, which was expected to be produced by the contact between hydrogen ions in the solution and Ti. The reaction formula is given by Equation (6). The TiH_2 dehydrogenation behavior of the product was studied by several researchers who found that it is relatively easily removed by vacuum heat treatment at 700 °C [18].

$$Ti + 2H^+ + 2e^- \rightarrow TiH_2, \Delta G^0{}_{50°C} = -101.769 \text{ kJ/mole} \tag{6}$$

The formation of the TiH_2 phase during leaching is disadvantageous to the processing, as additional steps will be required for its removal, thus incurring extra time and cost. On the other hand, the presence of TiH_2 is advantageous because it is insoluble in water and resistant to acidic solutions. Pure Ti metal can be easily produced through the heat treatment of TiH_2 [19].

The results of XRD analysis confirm that the MgO phase remains, regardless of the concentration of the acid. The remaining MgO is presumed to be produced by the decomposition of $Mg(OH)_2$.

For this, we confirmed the reaction occurrence from the HSC chemistry software and found that the reaction occurs at 600 °C or higher [20]. The reaction formula is given by Equation (7). This result agrees with a former report by Haoliang Dong et al., which MgO was obtained by $Mg(OH)_2$ calcined at different temperatures (500–700 °C) and durations (2–48 h) [21].

$$Mg(OH)_2 \rightarrow MgO + H_2O(l), \Delta G^0{}_{600°C} = -5.269 \text{ kJ/mole} \tag{7}$$

To quantitatively measure the amount of MgO in Group 1, Rietveld refinement was applied to the TOPAS software (structure analysis software, Bruker, Billerica, MA, USA), which revealed that the concentration of MgO decreases from 1–1 to 1–4, being 19%, 15.8%, 14.22%, and 12.2%, respectively [22]. The fraction of MgO decreases as the concentration of HCl increases. It is thought that the amount of HCl used as the leaching solution was insufficient to remove Mg and MgO produced in the combustion synthesis process. A previous study removed the by-products by leaching with acetic acid, followed by rinsing with HCl [7]. We used a sufficient amount of weak acid to remove any by-products, including Mg and MgO. A second leaching step was performed using a strong acid to remove any residual impurities.

The enthalpy and Gibbs free energy of HCl and acetic acid were calculated, and the results are listed in Table 2 [20]. The calculated results show that the temperature is the same as when acetic acid is used, while the enthalpy and Gibbs free energy are higher than those obtained when HCl is used, respectively. We deduced that using acetic acid increases the driving force of the reaction. Hence, we used acetic acid for Group 2. The XRD profiles of the Group 2 reaction products are shown in Figure 5.

As mentioned above, in experiment 2–1, the by-products were first removed by using 8.75 M acetic acid, while the remaining by-products were removed using 6.5 M HCl. In experiment 2–2, the by-products were first removed using 0.6 M HCl, followed by another removal using 6.5 M HCL. The XRD analysis of the reaction products were measured and the results were compared. Under both the conditions, the MgO and Mg by-products were successfully removed; however, the Ti oxide and Ti hydride phases remained. To remove these, we replaced acetic acid with HCl.

Table 2. Calculated reaction enthalpy and Gibbs free energy with hydrochloric acid and acetic acid.

Ti + MgO + Mg + 4HCl → Ti + H₂O(g) + H₂(g)			Ti + MgO + Mg + 4CH₃COOH → Ti + 2Mg(CH₃COO)₂ + H₂O(g) + H₂(g)	
Temp. (°C)	ΔH (kJ)	ΔG (kJ)	ΔH (kJ)	ΔG (kJ)
10	−213.557	−328.134	−645.888	−488.862
20	−217.321	−332.114	−627.825	−483.641
30	−220.731	−335.971	−612.213	−478.991
40	−223.968	−339.720	−598.095	−474.830
50	−227.133	−343.366	−584.942	−471.104
60	−230.256	−346.915	−572.584	−467.772
70	−233.373	−350.370	−560.828	−464.802
80	−236.525	−353.734	−549.498	−462.168
90	−239.732	−357.008	−538.522	−459.850
100	−243.019	−360.193	−527.840	−457.830

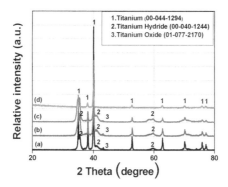

Figure 5. XRD profiles of reaction products: (**a**) experiment 2–1 (8.5 M CH₃COOH, 6.5 M HCl), (**b**) experiment 2–2 (0.6 M HCl, 6.5 M HCl), (**c**) experiment 2–3 (0.6 M HCl, 7.5 M HCl), and (**d**) experiment 2–4 (0.4 M HCl, 7.5 M HCl).

Experiment 2–3 was essentially the same as experiment 2–2, with the first leaching process performed using 0.6 M HCl. In the second step, the concentration of HCl was slightly higher than that used in experiment 2–2 (i.e., 7.5 M). The resulting product was subjected to XRD analysis (Figure 5). Similar to experiments 2–1 and 2–2, in experiment 2–3, the Mg and MgO peaks were not detected, while the Ti oxide and Ti hydride phases were still present.

In all the three experiments, we detected Ti oxide, which was not detected after the combustion synthesis. As shown in Figure 6a–c, when acetic acid and HCl were used, the temperature increased sharply during the acid-leaching process. This was caused by an exothermic reaction that occurred when MgO and Mg surrounding the Ti exothermically reacted with each other. MgO melted and the heat was transferred to the Ti surface, which reacted with the oxygen ions present in the solution to form an oxide film on the Ti powder surface. This is presumed to be the reason for the detection of Ti oxide. Figure 7 is a schematic illustration of Ti oxide formation.

To confirm the formation of Ti oxide under all the three conditions and to control the exothermic reaction, the concentration of acid used in the first leaching step was decreased from 0.6 M to 0.4 M. Similarly, to control the temperature, distilled water was used. In the second leaching step, 7.5 M HCl was used in the same way as in experiment 2–3. The XRD profile of the product (Figure 5d) show that Ti oxide was not formed because an exothermic reaction did not occur during the reaction, while MgO and Mg were completely removed. Here, a single Ti phase was detected.

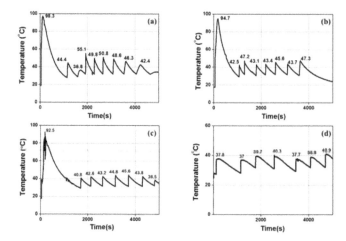

Figure 6. Temperature of leaching solution during two-step acid leaching process: (**a**) experiment 2–1 (8.5 M CH$_3$COOH, 6.5 M HCl), (**b**) experiment 2–2 (0.6 M HCl, 6.5 M HCl), (**c**) experiment 2–3 (0.6 M HCl, 7.5 M HCl), and (**d**) experiment 2–4 (0.4 M HCl, 7.5 M HCl).

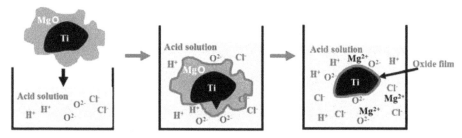

Figure 7. Ti oxide formation during leaching in experiments 2–1 to 2–3.

To identify the morphology of the reaction product and its purity, a sample produced in experiment 2–4 was subjected to FE-SEM and EDS analyses. The results of the analysis are shown in Figure 8. The prepared Ti powder exhibited an irregular shape, and the EDS results revealed that the Ti powder contained no impurities at all.

Figure 8. Morphology and purity of reaction product of experiment 2–4 (0.4 M HCl, 7.5 M HCl): (**a**) FE-SEM image and (**b**) EDS analysis result.

The oxygen contents of the Ti powders prepared according to Groups 1 and 2 leaching experimental conditions were measured using an NO/H analyzer. The results are shown in Figure 9. The concentration of MgO under each condition was about 10–19%, as mentioned above, for the first experiment. The second group of experiments also led to the formation of Ti oxides through an exothermic reaction between the reaction by-products and the acid solution in experiments 2–1 to 2–3, resulting in a remarkably high oxygen value. However, Ti oxide was not formed once the exothermic reaction was controlled by increasing the amount of distilled water used in experiment 2–4, and all the by-products were removed, leaving only the Ti single phase with an oxygen content of about 1.0 wt%.

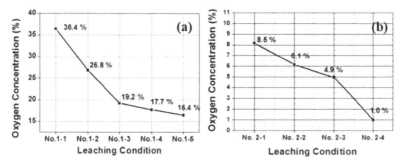

Figure 9. Oxygen contents of Ti powders as final product produced under experimental conditions of (a) Group 1 and (b) Group 2.

However, during acid leaching, where it is necessary to prepare the Ti powder when Ti oxide is formed, the reduction to Ti metal was very difficult in experiments 2–1 to 2–3. For example, Ti oxides such as TiO_2 have been reported to be more difficult to reduce because the Gibbs free energy required for reduction to Ti metal is 0.83 times less than that required for TiO_2 [14]. Nersisyan et al. reported that the oxygen content of Ti powder after SHS and leaching with nitric acid was 1.5 wt%. To further decrease the oxygen content, they performed deoxygenation with Ca. After deoxygenation, they found that the oxygen content had decreased to about 0.2–0.3 wt% [2]. Similarly, Okabe et al. reported that the oxygen content was 0.28 wt% for the Ti powder prepared using the PRP process [7]. For comparison, the Ti powder prepared in the present study had an oxygen content of about 1 wt% immediately after acid leaching and without any further steps.

4. Conclusions

Removal of by-products including Mg and MgO was studied using the magnesiothermic reduction of Ti powders in an SHS process. Ti oxide was used as the raw material and Mg was used as the reducing agent. To remove any unnecessary by-products such as Mg and MgO, acid leaching was used. HCl was chosen as the leaching solution and the efficiency of leaching was estimated by varying the concentration of the HCl. It was determined that two-step leaching with HCl effectively removed the by-products. In the first step, a low concentration of HCl was used, while a high concentration was used in the next step. Acid leaching with HCl is simpler than the conventional process in which complex experimental variants are used. The total oxygen content of the Ti powder immediately after leaching was found to be about 1 wt%, which is thought to be an advantage in terms of process simplicity and economy. The use of heat treatment would further lower the oxygen content.

The authors intend to undertake further in-depth studies to confirm the location of the remaining oxygen. That is, we will confirm whether the oxygen exists on the surface of the Ti powder or as an interstitial impurity. This will be the subject of a future report.

Author Contributions: S.H.C.: Investigation, methodology, writing—original draft; J.J.S.: Investigation; J.H.L.: Software; S.J.S.: Resources; D.W.K.: Validation; S.K.H.: Supervision; K.-T.P.: Funding acquisition, project administration, writing—-review & editing.

Funding: This research was funded by the Technology Innovation Program (Grant No. 10063427) funded by the Ministry of Trade, Industry & Energy and partially funded by an internal R&D program of the Korea Institute of Industrial Technology (KITECH) funded by the Ministry of Strategy and Finance, Republic of Korea.

Conflicts of Interest: The authors declare no conflict of interest.

References

1. Won, C.W.; Nersisyan, H.H.; Won, H.I. Titanium powder prepared by a rapid exothermic reaction. *Chem. Eng. J.* **2010**, *157*, 270–275. [CrossRef]
2. Nersisyan, H.H.; Won, H.I.; Won, C.W.; Jo, A.; Kim, J.H. Direct magnesiothermic reduction of titanium dioxide to titanium powder through combustion synthesis. *Chem. Eng. J.* **2014**, *235*, 67–74. [CrossRef]
3. Zheng, H.; Okabe, T.H. Selective chlorination of titanium ore and production of titanium powder by preform reduction process (PRP). In Proceedings of the 16th Iketani Conference, Tokyo, Japan, 12–16 November 2006.
4. Zheng, H.; Okabe, T.H. Production of titanium powder directly from titanium ore by preform reduction process (PRP). In Proceedings of the 5th UT^2 Graduate Student Workshop (University of Tokyo-University of Toronto), Tokyo, Japan, 7 June 2006.
5. Chen, G.Z.; Fray, D.J.; Farthing, T.W. Direct electrochemical reduction of titanium dioxide to titanium in molten calcium chloride. *Nature* **2000**, *47*, 361–363. [CrossRef]
6. Suzuki, R.O.; Ono, K.; Teranuma, K. Calciothermic reduction of titanium oxide and in-situ electrolysis in molten $CaCl_2$. *Metall. Mater. Trans. B* **2003**, *34*, 287–295. [CrossRef]
7. Okabe, T.H.; Oda, T.; Mitsuda, Y. Titanium powder production by preform reduction process (PRP). *J. Alloys Compd.* **2004**, *364*, 156–163. [CrossRef]
8. Chen, W.; Yamamoto, Y.; Peter, W.H.; Gorti, S.B.; Sabau, A.S.; Clark, M.B.; Nunn, S.D.; Kiggans, J.O.; Blue, C.A.; Williams, J.C.; et al. Cold compaction study of Armstrong process Ti-6Al-4V powders. *Powder Technol.* **2011**, *214*, 194–199. [CrossRef]
9. Chen, W.; Yamamoto, Y.; Peter, W.H.; Clark, M.B.; Nunn, S.D.; Kiggans, J.O.; Muth, T.R.; Blue, C.A.; Williams, J.C.; Akhtar, K. The investigation of die-pressing and sintering behavior of ITP CP-Ti and Ti-6Al-4V powders. *J. Alloys Compd.* **2012**, *541*, 440–447. [CrossRef]
10. Xia, Y.; Fang, Z.Z.; Zhang, Y.; Lefler, H.; Zhang, T.; Sun, P.; Huang, Z. Hydrogen assisted magnesiothermic reduction (HAMR) of commercial TiO_2 to produce titanium powder with controlled morphology and particle size. *Mater. Trans.* **2017**, *58*, 355–360. [CrossRef]
11. Kapias, T.; Griffiths, R.F. Accidental releases of titanium tetrachloride ($TiCl_4$) in the context of major hazards-spill behavior using REACTPOOL. *J. Hazard. Mater.* **2005**, *A119*, 41–52. [CrossRef] [PubMed]
12. Okabe, T.H.; Hamanaka, Y.; Taninouchi, Y. Direct oxygen removal technique for recycling titanium using molten $MgCl_2$ salt. *Faraday Discuss.* **2016**, *190*, 109–126. [CrossRef] [PubMed]
13. Choi, S.H.; Ali, B.; Hyun, S.K.; Sim, J.J.; Choi, W.J.; Joo, W.; Lim, J.H.; Lee, Y.J.; Kim, T.S.; Park, K.T. Fabrication of a spherical titanium powder by combined combustion synthesis and DC plasma treatment. *Arch. Metall. Mater.* **2017**, *62*, 1057–1062. [CrossRef]
14. Bolivar, R.; Friedrich, B. Synthesis of titanium via magnesiothermic reduction of TiO_2 (pigment). In Proceedings of the EMC, Kyoto, Japan, 20–24 July 2009.
15. HSC Chemistry Software ver. 8.0, Eh-pH Diagrams Module, Outotec. 2014. Available online: https://www.outotec.com (accessed on 20 November 2018).
16. Brown, P.L.; Ekberg, C. *Hydrolysis of Metal Ions*; Wiley-VCH: Weinheim, Germany, 2016; pp. 180, 194.
17. Won, Y.R.; Kim, D.S. Studies on the effect of temperature on lead ion in aqueous environment based on pourbaix diagram. *J. Korea Soc. Waste Manag.* **2013**, *30*, 60–67. [CrossRef]
18. Qian, M.; Froes, F.H. *Titanium Powder Metallurgy: Science, Technology and Applications*; Elsevier Inc.: Amsterdam, The Netherlands, 2015.
19. Fang, Z.Z.; Middlemas, S.; Guo, J.; Fan, P. A new, energy-efficient chemical pathway for extracting Ti metal from Ti minerals. *J. Am. Chem. Soc.* **2013**, *135*, 18248–18251. [CrossRef] [PubMed]
20. HSC Chemistry Software ver. 8.0, Reaction Equations Module, Outotec. 2014. Available online: https://www.outotec.com (accessed on 20 November 2018).

Metals **2019**, *9*, 169

21. Dong, H.; Unluer, C.; Al-Tabbaa, A.; Yang, E.H. Characterization of MgO Calcined from Mg(OH)$_2$ Produced from Reject Brine. In Proceedings of the Fourth International Conference on Sustainable Construction Materials and Technologies, Las Vegas, NV, USA, 7–11 August 2016.
22. TOPAS Software ver. 5.0, Rietveld Refinement Module, Bruker. 2014. Available online: https://www.bruker.com/products/x-ray-diffraction-and-elemental-analysis/x-ray-diffraction/xrd-software/topas.html (accessed on 17 August 2018).

metals

Article

Microstructure and Magnetic Properties of Mn$_{55}$Bi$_{45}$ Powders Obtained by Different Ball Milling Processes

Xiang Li [1], Dong Pan [1], Zhen Xiang [2], Wei Lu [2,*] and Dan Batalu [3]

[1] School of Materials Science and Engineering, University of Shanghai for Science and Technology, Shanghai 200093, China; xiangli@usst.edu.cn (X.L.); pandong9109@163.com (D.P.)

[2] Shanghai Key Laboratory of Development & Application for Metal-Functional Materials, School of Materials Science and Engineering, Tongji University, Shanghai 200092, China; xiangzhen@tongji.edu.cn

[3] Materials Science and Engineering Faculty, University Politehnica of Bucharest, Bucharest 060042, Romania; dan.batalu@upb.ro

* Correspondence: weilu@tongji.edu.cn; Tel.: +86-136-8184-5641

Received: 20 March 2019; Accepted: 11 April 2019; Published: 15 April 2019

Abstract: Low-temperature phase (LTP) MnBi is considered as a promising rare-earth-free permanent magnetic material with high coercivity and unique positive temperature coefficient of coercivity. Mn$_{55}$Bi$_{45}$ ribbons with high purity of LTP MnBi phase were prepared by melt spinning. Then, Mn$_{55}$Bi$_{45}$ powders with different particle size were obtained by low-energy ball milling (LEBM) with and without added surfactant. The coercivity is enhanced in both cases. Microstructure characterization reveals that Mn$_{55}$Bi$_{45}$ powders obtained by surfactant assisted low-energy ball milling (SALEBM) have better particle size uniformity and show higher decomposition of LTP MnBi. Coercivity can achieve a value of 17.2 kOe and the saturation magnetization (M_s) is 16 emu/g when Mn$_{55}$Bi$_{45}$ powders milled about 10 h by SALEBM. Coercivity has achieved a maximum value of 18.2 kOe at room temperature, and 23.5 kOe at 380 K after 14 h of LEBM. Furthermore, Mn$_{55}$Bi$_{45}$ powders obtained by LEBM have better magnetic properties.

Keywords: Mn$_{55}$Bi$_{45}$ powders; low-energy ball milling; surfactant; particle size; coercivity; microstructure; magnetic properties

---

1. Introduction

Permanent magnets are indispensable components used in many vital areas including electric vehicles, medical equipment, high-energy product motors and generators, etc. [1,2]. Due to reserve crisis and high-cost of rare earth elements, there are a large amount of researches focusing on permanent magnets with reduced rare earth elements or rare earth-free permanent magnets [3–6].

Low-temperature phase (LTP) MnBi has been considered as a promising rare-earth-free magnet with unique magnetic properties [7–10]. However, it is difficult to obtain a single phase of LTP MnBi alloy, as Mn tends to segregate from the liquid phase below the peritectic temperature of 719 K [11,12]. Yang et al. [7] studied that Mn segregation can be reduced by melt-spinning process, in addition Mn$_{55}$Bi$_{45}$ can promote the formation of high purity LTP MnBi alloy. When MnBi powders mixed with other magnetic materials, the MnBi-based composites with high magnetic performance will be obtained [13,14]. It is critical to this method that the size of the MnBi powders is comparable to the size of their single magnetic domain (~500 nm) in order to maximize the loading of the soft magnetic phase [15,16]. Moreover, low-energy ball milling (LEBM) is the most successful method for fabricating MnBi powders with this size wheras too high mechanical energy may lead to the rapid decomposition of LTP MnBi [16]. The coercivity can be significantly enhanced by ball milling process, as it promotes the increase of lattice strain and dislocation density, as well as the reduction of particle size [17,18]. Xie et al. [16] reported that Mn$_{55}$Bi$_{45}$ powders were prepared by arc melting method and finished with LEBM at cryogenic temperature, coercivity reaches its maximum at 8 h of ball milling. Moreover, the record of magnetization 71.2 emu/g has been achieved via milling for 8 h, heat treated, and ball milled for extra half an hour process. Li et al. [19] studied the magnetic properties of anisotropic MnBi powders after LEBM performed in heptane, coercivity increases to 16.1 kOe at 5 h. The coercivity reaches a maximum of 16.2 kOe after 35 min of surfactant assisted low-energy ball milling (SALEBM) for MnBi particles obtained by Kanari et al. [20]. There is still a room to improve the coercvity of MnBi after ball milling. Furthermore, the contribution of SALEBM and the effect of surface defects on magnetization, coercivity are deserved to investigate further [20,21].

In our work, $Mn_{55}Bi_{45}$ powders with different particle size were obtained by low-energy ball milling, with and without surfactant. The size of $Mn_{55}Bi_{45}$ powders obtained by SALEBM is more uniform. Moreover, the room-temperature coercivity is enhanced in both cases, with an increase to 17.2 kOe by SALEBM and to 18.2 kOe by LEBM.

2. Materials and Methods

Commercial high purity manganese (99.99%) and bismuth (99.99%) (produced by Northeast Nonferrous Metals Market Co., Ltd., Shenyang, China) were used for obtaining a $Mn_{55}Bi_{45}$ ingot by induction melting in argon gas. The ingot was then cut into some parts and each part is about 5 g. Further, the ingot was used to obtain $Mn_{55}Bi_{45}$ ribbons by single-roller melt spinning with a tangential speed of 40 m/s. The ribbons were annealed for 30 min at 573 K in vacuum. The annealed ribbons were manually crushed into powders. Then powders were ground using a pestle and agate mortar, and sieved through a # 300 mesh resulting the particle size down to less than 48 μm. The sieved powders were milled using 2 methods: (1) milled for 2–14 h in heptane (C_7H_{16}) with the addition of 10 wt% oleic acid (OA, $C_{18}H_{34}O_2$), and (2) milled for 2–38 h only in heptane. The milling speed was 120 rpm. Zirconia balls of 3 mm diameter were used, with a ball to powder weight ratio of 10:1. The milled $Mn_{55}Bi_{45}$ powders were mixed with epoxy resin and aligned in a magnetic field of 1.8 T.

The crystallographic structure of the samples was examined by DX-2700 X-ray diffraction (XRD, Fangyuan Instrument Co., Ltd., Dandong, China) with Cu Kα radiation ($\lambda = 1.5418$ Å). The content of XRD phase was calculated by JADE 9. Quanta FEG 450 scanning electron microscopy (SEM, FEI, Hillsboro, OR, USA) was used to examine the size and morphology of the powders. The magnetic properties were measured by physical property measurement system (PPMS, Quantum Design Inc., San Diego, CA, USA) with an applied field up to 30 kOe.

3. Results and Discussion

3.1. High Purity of LTP MnBi Ribbons

In order to obtain high purity of LTP MnBi, $Mn_{55}Bi_{45}$ ribbons were prepared by melt spinning at a speed of 40 m/s and subsequently annealed in vacuum. The XRD patterns of $Mn_{55}Bi_{45}$ ribbon powders before annealing and annealed at 573 K for 30 min are shown in Figure 1. The weight percent of LTP MnBi phase is higher in annealed $Mn_{55}Bi_{45}$ ribbon powders. Before annealing, there are mainly Mn and Bi phases with little LTP MnBi in the ribbons. After annealing, the ribbons contain high purity of LTP MnBi over 90 wt% with a little Mn and Bi phases. Because during the formation of LTP MnBi, Mn tends to segregate from MnBi liquid at peritectic temperature [11].

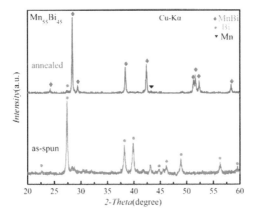

Figure 1. X-ray diffraction (XRD) patterns of Mn55Bi45 powders before and annealed at 573 K for 30 min.

The corresponding hysteresis loops of Mn55Bi45 powders before and after annealing are characterized and shown in Figure 2. The saturation magnetization (M_s) and coercivity are important magnetic parameters of a permanent magnet material which requires higher M_s and coercivity. M_s of the powders before annealing is 6.9 emu/g and achieves a higher value of 67 emu/g after annealing. The value of M_s is in accordance with the increase of LTP MnBi after annealing presented in Figure 1. Since the annealed Mn55Bi45 ribbons still contain a little Mn and Bi phases shown in Figure 1. M_s of annealed powders is close to the record of 71.2 emu/g achived by Xie et al. [16], but smaller than its theoretical value of 80 emu/g [22]. Coercivities of 7.4 kOe and 2.0 kOe are observed before and after annealing, respectively. Due to the sudden decrease in coercivity, it is desirable to obtain Mn55Bi45 powders with higher coercivity by different ball milling processes.

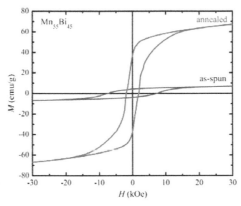

Figure 2. Hysteresis loops of Mn55Bi45 powders before and annealed at 573 K for 30 min.

3.2. Microstructure of Mn55Bi45 Powders Obtained by Different Ball Milling Processes

Figure 3 shows XRD patterns of Mn55Bi45 powders obtained by LEBM and SALEBM at different milling time. As shown in Figure 3a–e, the peak intensity of the LTP MnBi phase decreases, while characteristic peak of Bi and Mn phases gradually increase with prolonging the milling time, due to the partial decomposition of LTP MnBi during the ball milling processes [16]. The Bi phase has become the main phase of Mn55Bi45 powders in Figure 3e. The content of LTP MnBi phase decreases further when Mn55Bi45 powders is obtained by SALEBM, as shown in Figure 3c,e. As seen in Figure 3e, the reflection of Bi phase at 27.3° of Mn55Bi45 powders obtained by SALEBM at 14h significantly increases, and the weight percentage of LTP MnBi decreases to 42 wt%. This indicates that the added surfactant (OA) leads to a higher decomposition of LTP MnBi.

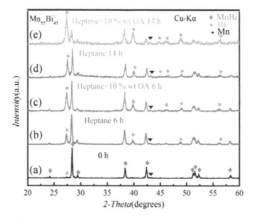

Figure 3. XRD patterns of Mn₅₅Bi₄₅ powders obtained by different ball milling processes at different milling time: (**a**) After annealing, (**b**) By LEBM at 6 h, (**c**) By SALEBM at 6 h, (**d**) By LEBM at 14 h and (**e**) By SALEBM at 14h.

In order to further explore the effect of different ball milling processes, microstructure of Mn₅₅Bi₄₅ powders was investigated. SEM images of the Mn₅₅Bi₄₅ obtained by SALEBM and by LEBM at different milling time are shown in Figures 4 and 5, respectively. The reduced size of Mn₅₅Bi₄₅ powders can be observed with the increase of time.

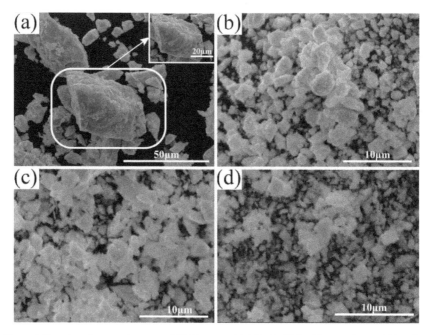

Figure 4. Scanning electron microscopy (SEM) images of (**a**) Crushed Mn₅₅Bi₄₅ powders and Mn₅₅Bi₄₅ powders obtained by SALEBM at (**b**) 4 h, (**c**) 10 h, (**d**) 14 h.

Figure 5. SEM images of Mn$_{55}$Bi$_{45}$ powders obtained by LEBM at (**a**) 4 h, (**b**) 10 h, (**c**) 14 h, (**d**) 34 h.

As seen in Figures 4a and 5a, coarse particles with small flaky particles on the their surfaces are mainly observed. As shown in Figure 4a, Mn$_{55}$Bi$_{45}$ ribbons was manually crushed and the size of resulted powders range between 1–40 μm before milling. The size distribution of SALEBM at 4 h is ~2 μm in Figure 4b. Figure 4b–d shows that the size of Mn$_{55}$Bi$_{45}$ powders obtained by SALEBM was reduced to ~4 μm, ~2 μm, and ~0.8 μm after 4, 10 and 14 h, respectively. The particles after 10 h of SALEBM have a size distribution of ~1 μm, as shown in Figure 4c. The size of powders is uniform and the shape is very regular. The size of Mn$_{55}$Bi$_{45}$ powders after 10 h of SALEBM is more homogenous. Agglomeration of the powders forms due to the surfactant molecules exist in the powders, as shown in Figure 4b,c. As shown in Figure 4d, Mn$_{55}$Bi$_{45}$ powders have less agglomerates, because the surfactant molecules have been adsorbed at the surface of powders [20]. As seen in Figure 5, the size of Mn$_{55}$Bi$_{45}$ powders obtained by LEBM (without surfactant) was reduced to ~14 μm, ~8 μm, and ~2.5 μm after 4, 10 and 14 h, respectively. The size distribution of LEBM is ~3 μm and ~2 μm after 10 and 14 h in Figure 5b,c, respectively. The size of powders is different, and the shape of particles is polyhedral which is very irregular. As shown in Figure 5d, the size of Mn$_{55}$Bi$_{45}$ powders obtained at 34 h by LEBM is ~0.7 μm which tends to equalize. This size becomes smaller and more uniform which cannot further be reduced, the coarse powders finally reduced down to finer particles. Compared Figure 4 with Figure 5, at the same milling time (<14 h), the powders size of SALEBM is smaller than the size of LEBM. Therefore, the added surfactant (OA) helps Mn$_{55}$Bi$_{45}$ powders to be milled with a higher size refinement and uniformity at shorter time, with the drawback of a higher decomposition of LTP MnBi shown in Figure 3.

3.3. Magnetic Properties of Mn$_{55}$Bi$_{45}$ Powders Obtained by Different Ball Milling Processes

To further investigated the contribution of different ball milling processes, the magnetic properties of Mn$_{55}$Bi$_{45}$ powders were measured. Hysteresis loops and variation of coercivity, M_s with milling time of Mn$_{55}$Bi$_{45}$ powders obtained by SALEBM and LEBM are shown in Figures 6 and 7, respectively. M_s gradually decreases with the increase of time, this is in agreement with the decreasing weight percentage of the LTP MnBi phase in Figure 3. The coercivity is simultaneously enhanced from 2.0 kOe at 0 h to a maximum due to the smaller particle size is less than the single domain size [23]. It is also important for a permanent magnet to achieve higher ratio of remanence (M_r) to M_s (M_r/M_s) and magnetic energy product $(BH)_{max}$. The change of the main magnetic properties such as M_s, coercivity, M_r/M_s, and $(BH)_{max}$ of $Mn_{55}Bi_{45}$ powders obtained by SALEBM and LEBM after different milling time are listed in Table 1.

As shown in Figure 6 and Table 1, $Mn_{55}Bi_{45}$ powders show a maximum coercivity of 17.2 kOe when milled 10 h by SALEBM. Coercivity achieves a maximum value of 18.2 kOe when $Mn_{55}Bi_{45}$ powders milled for 14 h by LEBM, as seen in Figure 7 and Table 1. The room-temperature coercivity is enhanced in both cases. The particle refinement and the increase of the stresses or the defects during ball milling process increases the coercivity [17,18]. This conclusion is in accordance with the refined microstructure of $Mn_{55}Bi_{45}$ powders shown in Figures 4 and 5. Figure 7b and Table 1 show that coercivity fast increased to 13.1 kOe after 2 h of milling by LEBM, achieving a higher value than 5.6 kOe by SALEBM at 2 h. Since coercivity depends on the microstructure, different sizes and irregular shapes of $Mn_{55}Bi_{45}$ powders shown in Figure 5 are beneficial to coercivity. Hence, LEBM is a more favorable method to significantly improve the coercivity. As shown in Figure 6 and Table 1, M_s drops to 43, 19, 16, and 9 emu/g when milled by SALEBM for 2, 6, 10, and 14 h, respectively. On the contrary, as shown in Figure 7, M_s drops to 52, 32, 20, 16, and 10 emu/g when milled by LEBM for 2, 6, 10, 14, and 18 h, respectively. The decomposition of the LTP MnBi will reduce the magnetization of the MnBi alloy [24]. $Mn_{55}Bi_{45}$ powders after ball milling with long time contain a large volume fraction of nonmagnetic Bi phase, hence a lower M_s is expected and confirmed by measurements, which reduces to 1 emu/g after 38 h of SALEBM shown in Figure 7. Figures 6 and 7 indicate that M_s of $Mn_{55}Bi_{45}$ powders decreases more rapidly when milled by SALEBM, this result is in agreement with the content of LTP MnBi phase decreases more rapidly (Figure 3).

As shown in Table 1, M_r/M_s of $Mn_{55}Bi_{45}$ powders increases from 55.1% at 0 h to 91.1% at 6 h of SALEBM and 90.0% at 4h of LEBM. It reveals that most of milled powders are aligned to the c-axis. However, M_r/M_s of SALEBM decreases more quickly indicating the powders of LEBM are better aligned to the c-axis [9]. $(BH)_{max}$ increase from 2.54 MGOe before milling to 4.2 MGOe after 2 h of SALEBM. $(BH)_{max}$ is 7.1 MGOe after 2 h of LEBM, which is equal to the value of 7.1 MGOe after 7 h of grinding reported by Yang et al. [22]. Moreover, all $(BH)_{max}$ of $Mn_{55}Bi_{45}$ powders obtained by LEBM are bigger. Therefore, $Mn_{55}Bi_{45}$ powders obtained by LEBM have better magnetic properties.

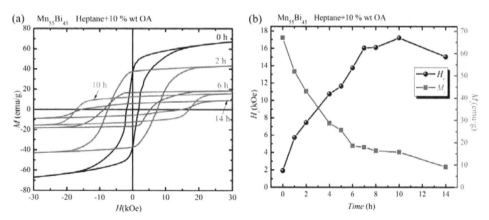

Figure 6. (**a**) Hysteresis loops and (**b**) Variation of coercivity, M_s with milling time of $Mn_{55}Bi_{45}$ powders obtained by SALEBM.

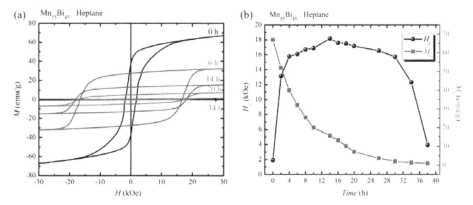

Figure 7. (**a**) Hysteresis loops and (**b**) Variation of coercivity, M_s with milling time of $Mn_{55}Bi_{45}$ powders obtained by LEBM.

Table 1. Change of the main magnetic properties of $Mn_{55}Bi_{45}$ powders obtained by different ball milling processes after different milling time.

Sample	M_s (emu/g)	H_c (kOe)	M_r/M_s (%)	$(BH)_{max}$ (MGOe)
Heptane + 10 wt% OA (2h)	43	7.5	86.9	4.2
Heptane (2h)	52	13.1	89.9	7.1
Heptane + 10 wt% OA (4h)	27	10.8	88.3	2.0
Heptane (4h)	40	15.8	90.0	4.1
Heptane + 10 wt% OA (6h)	19	13.8	91.1	0.9
Heptane (6h)	32	16.1	85.3	2.3
Heptane + 10 wt% OA (10h)	16	17.2	79.4	0.5
Heptane (10h)	20	16.9	84.6	1.0
Heptane + 10 wt% OA (14h)	9	15.1	65.1	0.1
Heptane (14h)	16	18.2	84.5	0.3

$Mn_{55}Bi_{45}$ powders obtained by LEBM for 14 h are selected to measure the high temperatures magnetic properties of MnBi powders. Figure 8 shows hysteresis loops at 300 K, 325 K, 350 K, 380 K and variation of coercivity, M_s with temperature. M_s decreases with with the incease of temperature. Coercivity of $Mn_{55}Bi_{45}$ powders increase to 23.5 kOe at 380 K. With the increase of temperature, coercivity rapidly increases exhibiting an unusual positive temperature coefficient of coercivity. This positive temperature coefficient of coercivity is related to the magnetocrystalline anisotropy of MnBi [7,25], owing to the non-uniform change of lattice constants with temperature [7].

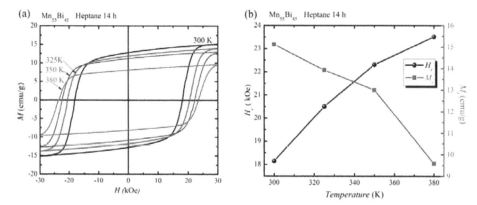

Figure 8. (a) Hysteresis loops at 300 K, 325 K, 350 K, 380 K and (b) Variation of coercivity, M_s with temperature of $Mn_{55}Bi_{45}$ powders obtained by LEBM for 14 h.

4. Conclusions

In conclusion, $Mn_{55}Bi_{45}$ ribbons with high purity of LTP MnBi were successfully prepared. Furthermore, $Mn_{55}Bi_{45}$ powders with different particle sizes were obtained by low-energy ball milling with and without surfactant (OA). M_s of powders obtained by both processes gradually decreases with the increase of time. $Mn_{55}Bi_{45}$ powders obtained by SALEBM have a higher size refinement and uniformity at shorter time, but with the drawbacks of higher decomposition of LTP MnBi and lower M_s. LEBM is a more favorable method to significantly improve the coercivity. Coercivity achieves a maximum value of 18.2 kOe at room temperature and 23.5 kOe at 380 K when MnBi powders milled 14 h by LEBM, without surfactant addition. Moreover, $Mn_{55}Bi_{45}$ powders obtained by LEBM have better magnetic properties. This approach can be applied to obtain MnBi-based composites with high magnetic performance.

Author Contributions: Conceptualization, W.L.; methodology, X.L. and X.Z.; validation, W.L.; formal analysis, D.P.; investigation, X.L. and W.L.; resources, X.L. and W.L.; data curation, X.L. and D.P.; writing—original draft preparation, X.L.; writing—review and editing, D.P. and D.B.; visualization, D.P. and X.Z.; supervision, X.Z. and D.B.; project administration, W.L.; funding acquisition, X.L., W.L. and D.B.

Funding: This work was supported by the Natural Science Foundation of Shanghai (No. 17ZR1419700), the National Natural Science Foundation of China (Grant No. 51671146), the Fundamental Research Funds for the Central Universities (No. 2016117), Shanghai Key Laboratory of Impression Evidence (No. 20163003), and by a grant of the Romanian Ministry of Research and Innovation, CCCDI-UEFISCDI, project number PN-III-P3-3.1-PM-RO-CN-2018-0113/17/2018, within PNCDI III.

Conflicts of Interest: The authors declare no conflict of interest.

References

1. Poudyal, N.; Liu, J.P. Advances in nanostructured permanent magnets research. *J. Phys. D Appl. Phys.* **2013**, *46*, 043001. [CrossRef]
2. Bailey, G.; Mancheri, N.; Van Acker, K. Sustainability of Permanent Rare Earth Magnet Motors in (H)EV Industry. *J. Sustain. Metall.* **2017**, *3*, 611–626. [CrossRef]
3. Cao, S.; Yue, M.; Yang, Y.X.; Zhang, D.T.; Liu, W.Q.; Zhang, J.X.; Guo, Z.H.; Li, W. Magnetic properties and thermal stability of MnBi/NdFeB hybrid bonded magnets. *J. Appl. Phys.* **2011**, *109*, 07A740. [CrossRef]
4. McCallum, R.W.; Lewis, L.; Skomski, R.; Kramer, M.J.; Anderson, I.E. Practical aspects of modern and future permanent magnets. *Annu. Rev. Mater. Res.* **2014**, *44*, 451–477. [CrossRef]
5. Kuz'min, M.D.; Skokov, K.P.; Jian, H.; Radulov, I.; Gutfleisch, O. Towards high performance permanent magnets without rare earths. *J. Phys. Condens. Matter* **2014**, *26*, 064205. [CrossRef]

6. Song, Y.M.; Xiang, Z.; Wang, T.L.; Niu, J.C.; Xia, K.D.; Lu, W.; Zhang, H.; Cao, Y.Z.; Yoshimura, S.; Saito, H. High temperature exchange bias effect in melt-spun $Mn_{55}Bi_{45}$ alloys. *Appl. Phys. Lett.* **2016**, *109*, 112402. [CrossRef]

7. Yang, J.B.; Yang, Y.B.; Chen, X.G.; Ma, X.B.; Han, J.Z.; Yang, Y.C.; Guo, S.; Yan, A.R.; Huang, Q.Z.; Wu, M.M.; et al. Anisotropic nanocrystalline MnBi with high coercivity at high temperature. *Appl. Phys. Lett.* **2011**, *99*, 082505. [CrossRef]

8. Saito, T.; Nishimura, R.; Nishio-Hamane, D. Magnetic properties of Mn-Bi melt-spun ribbons. *J. Magn. Magn. Mater.* **2014**, *349*, 9–14. [CrossRef]

9. Yang, Y.B.; Chen, X.G.; Guo, S.; Yan, A.R.; Huang, Q.Z.; Wu, M.M.; Chen, D.F.; Yang, Y.C.; Yang, J.B. Temperature dependences of structure and coercivity for melt-spun MnBi compound. *J. Magn. Magn. Mater.* **2013**, *330*, 106–110. [CrossRef]

10. Xiang, Z.; Song, Y.M.; Pan, D.; Shen, Y.L.; Qian, L.W.; Luo, Z.Y.; Liu, Y.S.; Yang, H.W.; Yan, H.; Lu, W. Coercivity enhancement and magnetization process in $Mn_{55}Bi_{45}$ alloys with refined particle size. *J. Alloys Compd.* **2018**, *744*, 432–437. [CrossRef]

11. Cui, J.; Choi, J.P.; Li, G.; Polikarpov, E.; Darsell, J.; Overman, N.; Olszta, M.; Schreiber, D.; Bowden, M.; Droubay, T.; et al. Thermal stability of MnBi magnetic materials. *J. Phys. Condens. Matter* **2014**, *26*, 064212. [CrossRef] [PubMed]

12. Oikawa, K.; Mitsui, Y.; Koyama, K.; Anzai, K. Thermodynamic Assessment of the Bi-Mn System. *Mater. Trans.* **2011**, *52*, 2032–2039. [CrossRef]

13. Lu, W.; Luo, Z.Y.; Xiang, Z.; Wang, X.; Pan, F.; Tian, W.; Yan, Y. Synthesis and magnetic properties of $LTP-Mn_{55}Bi_{45}/Fe_7Co_3$ and $LTP-Mn_{55}Bi_{45}/Co$ magnetic nanocomposites with enhanced energy product. *Mater. Lett.* **2019**, *236*, 514–516. [CrossRef]

14. Dai, Q.L.; Warsi, M.A.; Xiao, J.Q.; Ren, S.Q. Solution processed MnBi-FeCo magnetic nanocomposites. *Nano Res.* **2016**, *9*, 3222–3228. [CrossRef]

15. Nguyen, P.K.; Jin, S.; Berkowitz, A.E. Unexpected magnetic domain behavior in LTP-MnBi. *IEEE Trans. Magn.* **2013**, *49*, 3387–3390. [CrossRef]

16. Xie, W.; Polikarpov, E.; Choi, J.P.; Bowden, M.E.; Sun, K.W.; Cui, J. Effect of ball milling and heat treatment process on MnBi powders magnetic properties. *J. Alloys Compd.* **2016**, *680*, 1–5. [CrossRef]

17. Yousefi, M.; Sharafi, S.; Mehrolhosseiny, A. Correlation between structural parameters and magnetic properties of ball milled nanocrystalline Fe-Co-Si powders. *Adv. Powder Technol.* **2014**, *25*, 752–760. [CrossRef]

18. Mondal, B.N.; Sardar, G.; Nath, D.N.; Chattopadhyay, P.P. Ferromagnetic behavior of nanocrystalline Cu–Mn alloy prepared by ball milling. *J. Magn. Magn. Mater.* **2014**, *371*, 139–143. [CrossRef]

19. Li, B.B.; Ma, Y.L.; Shao, B.; Li, C.H.; Chen, D.M.; Sun, J.C.; Zheng, Q.; Yin, X. Preparation and magnetic properties of anisotropic MnBi powders. *Phys. B Condens. Matter* **2018**, *530*, 322–326. [CrossRef]

20. Kanari, K.; Sarafidis, C.; Gjoka, M.; Niarchos, D.; Kalogirou, O. Processing of magnetically anisotropic MnBi particles by surfactant assisted ball milling. *J. Magn. Magn. Mater.* **2017**, *426*, 691–697. [CrossRef]

21. Zhang, Y.F.; Han, J.Z.; Liu, S.Q.; Tian, H.D.; Zhao, H.; Du, H.L.; Yang, Y.C.; Fang, Y.K.; Li, W.; Yang, J.B. Structural modification and ultra-high coercivity of nanostructural anisotropic MnBi/Bi films. *Acta Mater.* **2017**, *128*, 96–102. [CrossRef]

22. Yang, Y.B.; Chen, X.G.; Wu, R.; Wei, J.Z.; Ma, X.B.; Han, J.Z.; Du, H.L.; Liu, S.Q.; Wang, C.S.; Yang, Y.C.; et al. Preparation and magnetic properties of MnBi. *J. Appl. Phys.* **2012**, *111*, 07E312. [CrossRef]

23. Rao, N.V.R.; Gabay, A.M.; Hu, X.; Hadjipanayis, G.C. Fabrication of anisotropic MnBi nanoparticles by mechanochemical process. *J. Alloys Compd.* **2014**, *586*, 349–352. [CrossRef]

24. Li, C.H.; Guo, D.L.; Shao, B.; Li, K.J.; Li, B.B.; Chen, D.M. Effect of heat treatment and ball milling on MnBi magnetic materials. *Mater. Res. Express* **2018**, *5*, 016104. [CrossRef]

25. Guo, X.; Chen, X.; Altounian, Z.; Ström-Olsen, J.O. Magnetic properties of MnBi prepared by rapid solidification. *Phys. Rev. B* **1992**, *46*, 14578–14582. [CrossRef]

Article

Mechanical Properties of Some Metallic Powder Alloys and Their Contribution to the Performance of Diamond Tools Used for Cutting Granite

Luís Guerra Rosa *, Carlos A. Anjinho, Pedro M. Amaral and Jorge Cruz Fernandes

IDMEC, DEM, Instituto Superior Técnico, Universidade de Lisboa, 1049-001 Lisboa, Portugal;
gancho.anjinho@gmail.com (C.A.A.); Pedro.Amaral@tecnico.ulisboa.pt (P.M.A.);
cruz.fernandes@tecnico.ulisboa.pt (J.C.F.)
* Correspondence: luisguerra@tecnico.ulisboa.pt; Tel.: +351-21-841-7280

Received: 29 October 2019; Accepted: 11 November 2019; Published: 13 November 2019

Abstract: This work examined some pre-alloyed cobalt-, iron-, and copper-based powder binder systems—such as those launched commercially under the brand names of Cobalite and Next—in terms of their as-sintered physical-mechanical properties, namely, apparent density, Young´s modulus, yield strength, rupture strength, rupture strain, toughness modulus, and Vickers hardness. These types of sintered products are traditionally used in the fabrication of diamond impregnated tools for cutting granite stones. The following powder binder systems were evaluated: Cobalite HDR pre-alloyed powder, Next 300 pre-alloyed powder, and four other mixtures of these with Cu and Fe powders: Cobalite HDR + 20 wt% Cu; Cobalite HDR + 20 wt% Fe; Next 300 + 20 wt% Cu; Next 300 + 20 wt% Fe. The evaluation methodology aimed to establish criteria for developing new diamond tools and, therefore, it included the measurement of several technological parameters directly related to the cutting performance of the tools (e.g., energy consumption measurements made exclusively in the tool drive motor, forces generated in the tool, tool consumption per unit weight of stone removed by the cutting). The results show the adequacy of the methodology for the optimisation of diamond retention capacity of these types of metal matrices and for improving the working performance of the diamond tools.

Keywords: cobalt-based alloy; pre-alloyed agglomerates; hot pressed sintering; mechanical properties; cutting performance; diamond impregnated tools; stone machining; tool wear

---

1. Introduction

Sintered powder metallurgy (PM) products are traditionally used in the fabrication of diamond impregnated tools (usually named "diamond tools" for short) for cutting natural stone or other hard materials, such as concrete or artificial stones. A huge variety of different types of petrous materials is used nowadays in architecture and sculpture. Compared to metal alloys, petrous materials (natural or man-made) usually show a more heterogeneous microstructure, and they can be much more difficult for machining (e.g., drilling, sawing, grinding, or polishing) in order to obtain the final shape. Depending on the hardness of their mineralogical constituents, some petrous materials are more difficult to cut than others, and therefore the concept of "relative abrasiveness" was introduced in a publication dated 1998, and therein [1] a method for the classification of ornamental stones according to the abrasiveness that they show during a processing operation, involving the removal of stock material by a tool, was presented.

It is due to their higher efficiency and longer service life that diamond tools are used for most stages of the machining process. For each type of stone and each stage of the machining process there will be an optimum tool, and therefore, in order to satisfy their costumers, tool manufacturers continuously provide the market with new and more efficient diamond tools [2,3].

In fact, the abrasiveness of petrous materials can be very severe and manufacturers of diamond tools are aware of that and make use of many types of commercially available metal powders which, after a consolidation process, play the role of "binders for diamond". The role of the binders is crucial for the performance of the diamond tools [4]. There are already several works dealing with the simulation by computer modelling of the retention of a synthetic diamond particle in a metallic matrix, e.g., [5–9], and there are other type of works aiming to understand the wear of materials with granitic textures (e.g., granite, granodiorite, gabbro, quartzite) while being processed by diamond tools [10,11].

Based on our own experience, the present work intends to demonstrate the experimental methodologies that can be used to assess the properties that are thought to be the most relevant ones in terms of the metallic binders. Our previous investigations [12,13] have shown that the wear of the PM matrices can be related to the resultant force (F_r) applied to the tool and with some mechanical properties of the PM matrix through the following empirical expression:

$$\Delta m = \alpha \cdot \frac{F_r}{\sigma_r^{0.6} \cdot T_m^{0.1} \cdot H_V^{0.5} \cdot E} \tag{1}$$

where Δm represents the matrix weight loss (per run of the tool), α is a constant of proportionality, σ_r is the rupture strength (ultimate tensile stress), T_m is the modulus of toughness, H_V is the Vickers hardness, and E is the Young's modulus.

Once the properties of different PM binders are determined after sintering, the tool manufacturer can then make decisions in order to produce the diamond tools using the selected binders. The way in which diamond tools can then afterwards be adequately tested under real industrial conditions is also presented in this work.

2. Materials and Methods

2.1. Starting Powders

Information on the starting powders is given in Table 1. Table 2 summarizes the chemical compositions of the PM mixtures studied in this work, which were: the Cobalite HDR pre-alloyed powder, the Next 300 pre-alloyed powder, and four other mixtures of these with copper or iron powders. Values of theoretical or maximum achievable density corresponding to a fully densified body are also shown in Table 2. The reason for adding Cu and Fe to the Cobalite and Next compositions was to investigate the influence of those additions in terms of change in microstructure and physical–mechanical properties. Depending on the type of tool and on the type of stone to be machined, manufacturers of diamond tools for stone processing also use these compositions with a higher content of Cu or higher content of Fe. For example, and just for clarification, the mixture named "Cobalite HDR + 20% Cu" in Table 2 consists of 20% pure Cu powder and 80% Cobalite HDR powder.

Table 1. Starting powders.

Powders Designation	Fisher Sub-Sieve Size (μm)	Supplier
Cobalite HDR	6–7	Umicore
Next 300	~4	Eurotungstene
Electrolytic Cu	11–12	Eurotungstene
Carbonyl Iron (>99.5% Fe)	7–8	Eurotungstene

According to the literature, the maximum density achievable with Cobalite HDR is 8.18 g/cm^3 [14] and with Next 300 is 8.12 g/cm^3 [15]. Once the percentages indicated in Table 2 are in weight, it is more appropriate to calculate the theoretical density values of the other powder combinations using an inverse rule of mixtures, and considering that the theoretical densities of copper and iron are 8.96 g/cm^3

and 7.87 g/cm^3, respectively. Then, for example, the theoretical density of the mixture Cobalite HDR + 20% Cu is given by the inverse of the sum of (0.8/theoretical density of Cobalite HDR) + (0.2/theoretical density of Copper).

Table 2. Chemical composition and theoretical density of the powder metallurgy (PM) mixtures.

Powders	Weight Percentage			Theoretical Density (g/cm^3)
	Co	Cu	Fe	
Cobalite HDR	27	7	66	8.18
Cobalite HDR + 20% Cu	21	26	53	8.33
Cobalite HDR + 20% Fe	21	6	73	8.12
Next 300	25	3	72	8.12
Next 300 + 20% Cu	20	22	58	8.28
Next 300 + 20% Fe	20	2	78	8.07

Powders were observed with an analytical scanning electron microscope (SEM, Hitachi S-2400, Japan) and examples of the SEM observations are depicted in Figure 1.

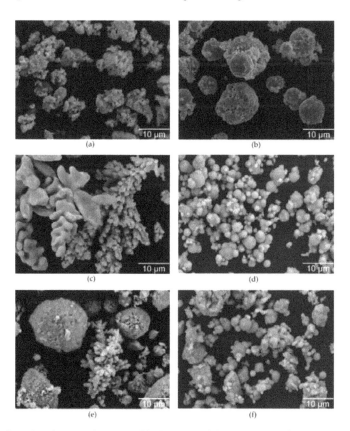

Figure 1. Scanning electron microscope (SEM) images of the starting powders: (**a**) Cobalite HDR powder; (**b**) Next 300 powder; (**c**) Cu powder; (**d**) Fe powder; (**e**) Cobalite HDR + 20% Cu; (**f**) Next 300 + 20% Fe.

2.2. Sintering of Metallic Binders

All powder mixtures were hot-pressed using graphite moulds and applying a uniaxial pressure of 33 MPa at a sintering temperature of 800 °C. The sintered bodies (no diamonds were involved) were rectangular prisms with final dimensions of $55 \times 11 \times 10$ mm^3 and were obtained in groups of six. Due to the electric current applied to the graphite mould, a sufficiently high heating rate was used to make it possible to go from room temperature to 800 °C in 3 min. Then, the holding time at 800 °C was also 3 min. At high temperature, a reducing atmosphere containing CO and CO_2 was generated inside the mould due to the reaction of the oxygen in the air with the graphite (carbon). This CO and CO_2-rich atmosphere protected the powders from oxidation. Figure 2a shows one of the sintered bodies, from which the specimens used for tensile testing were machined.

(a)   (b)

Figure 2. (a) Sintered body with dimensions of $55 \times 11 \times 10$ mm^3; (b) specimen used for tensile test.

The PM sintered bodies were observed by optical microscopy (OM) using an Olympus BX51M optical microscope; examples of the observations are depicted in Figure 3.

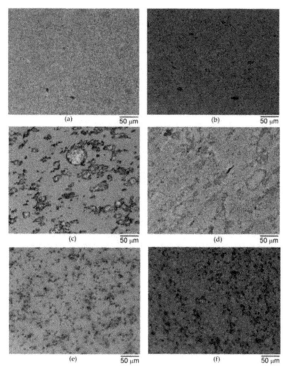

Figure 3. Optical observation of the microstructures of PM sintered bodies: (a) Cobalite HDR; (b) Next 300; (c) Cobalite HDR + 20% Cu; (d) Next 300 + 20% Cu; (e) Cobalite HDR + 20% Fe; (f) Next 300 + 20% Fe.

Besides optical microscopy, PM sintered bodies were also observed by SEM. Examples of those observations are shown in Figure 4. It must be clarified that, from our observations by OM and SEM, we did not notice any problem of binding between the Cu or Fe particles and the Cobalite HDR or Next 300 matrices.

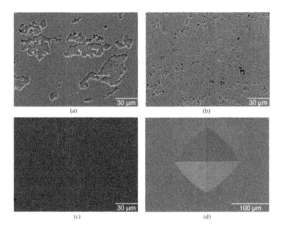

Figure 4. SEM observations of the microstructures of PM sintered bodies: (**a**) Cobalite HDR + 20% Cu; (**b**) Next 300 + 20% Fe; (**c**) Cobalite HDR; (**d**) Vickers indentation in Cobalite HDR.

2.3. Characterisation of Metallic Binders

Physical-mechanical characterisation of the metallic binders was carried out by determining several properties. Table 3 presents the list of properties that were determined, as well as the corresponding methodology, equipment, and total number of specimens that were used for their determination.

Table 3. Properties, methodologies, equipment, and number of specimens.

Property	Methodology	Equipment	No. of Specimens for Each Type of Binder
Apparent density	Water immersion technique	Electronic Densimeter EW-200SG	4
Vickers hardness	Indentation test	Mitutoyo AVK-C2 hardness tester (using a load of 1 kgf)	3
Dynamic Young´s modulus	Resonance frequency	RFDA from IMCE (see Figure 5)	3
Yield strength, Rupture strength, Strain at rupture, Modulus of toughness	Stress-strain curves from tensile tests [1] on cylindrical specimens	Instron model 8502	3

[1] Crosshead speed: 0.5 mm/min.

Figure 5. RFDA (Resonant Frequency and Damping Analyser) equipment (made by IMCE, Genk, Belgium) used for measuring the dynamic Young´s modulus.

In addition to measurements of important properties, like apparent density, Vickers hardness, and dynamic Young's modulus, tensile tests were conducted in cylindrical specimens using an Instron strain gauge extensometer (Instron, Norwood, MA, USA), 25 mm gauge, +100–10% max strain. The tensile tests allowed the determination of yield strength a 0.2% offset, $\sigma_{0.2}$, and also of: rupture strength (ultimate tensile stress),

$$\sigma_r = \frac{F_{max}}{A_0}, \tag{2}$$

strain at rupture,

$$\varepsilon_r = \frac{L_f - L_0}{L_0} \times 100\%, \tag{3}$$

modulus of toughness,

$$T_m = \frac{\sigma_{0.2} + \sigma_r}{2} \varepsilon_r, \tag{4}$$

where F_{max} is the maximum force, A_0 is the initial cross-section area of the specimen, L_f is the distance between the reference points of the specimens at the moment of rupture, and L_0 is the initial distance between those points or gauge length. The modulus of toughness is the amount of strain energy per unit volume (i.e., strain energy density) that a material can absorb just before it fractures. The modulus of toughness is calculated as the area under the stress-strain curve up to the fracture point, and for simplification purposes Equation (4) was used as an approximation.

2.4. Characterisation of Diamond Tools

2.4.1. Type of Diamond Tools

Figure 6 shows the types of tools used in this study. This type of disc is typically used in the industry for grinding granite and other hard stones. Each grinding wheel was composed of 16 diamond-impregnated segments; each segment was 24 mm long, 20 mm wide, and was initially 5 mm thick. The steel disc to which the segments were brazed had an external diameter of 150 mm and a thickness of 18 mm.

Figure 6. Type of grinding wheel used in this study.

For easier comparison of their performance, the grinding wheels were manufactured so that the only difference between them was the binder that held the diamonds. The concentration and grit of the diamond was kept constant. The diamonds were MBS 940 produced by General Electric, 40–50 mesh size. The content of diamonds in the segments was 2.5 wt%. The segments for the grinding wheels of Cobalite HDR and Next 300 were obtained using the same hot-pressing processing variables indicated in Section 2.2, with the only difference in the size of the graphite mould used.

2.4.2. Stone Samples

The granite used for evaluating the performance of the grinding wheels was from Portalegre district, Portugal, and it is commercially sold under the designation of SPI or Azul Alpalhão. Each stone tile had dimensions of $300 \times 300 \times 20$ mm^3. The apparent density of the Azul Alpalhão granite was 2.66 g/cm^3 and it was determined according to test standard EN 1936:2008.

2.4.3. Test Procedure

The grinding tests were carried out with the IST-Lisbon Classification Equipment (see Figure 7). The first version of this equipment was commissioned in 1997, but since then new versions have been constructed. Detailed description of the IST-Lisbon Classification Equipment can be found in other publications [16–18] and the measurements made with it allow the determination of the following parameters: the parameter Z representing the electric energy consumption per unit mass of removed stone; the parameter ϕ, which represents the mass loss of the tool per unit mass of removed stone; the force F_v, defined as the mean value of vertical load measurements monitored (and data stored) during the grinding operation; the force F_h, defined as the mean value of horizontal load measurements monitored (and data stored) during the grinding operation.

Using the abovementioned parameters it is then possible to obtain two other quantities: (i) the stone "relative abrasiveness" towards the used tool, expressed by the parameter A so that:

$$A = Z \times \phi, \tag{5}$$

and (ii) the resultant force F_r, generated by the contact between the tool and the granite, which is given by:

$$F_r = \sqrt{F_v^2 + F_h^2} \tag{6}$$

(a)   (b)

Figure 7. (a) General view of the IST-Lisbon Classification Equipment; (b) detail of a grinding test, showing several grooves made at the surface of a granite tile.

To allow the comparison of results obtained from several tools, the worktable velocity and the rotational speed of the tool, as well as the water flow, were kept constant during the tests (see Table 4). The tests were conducted with the discs rotating in downcut conditions [18] towards the tile of the granite.

Table 4. Working parameters of downcut conditions used in the tests.

Rotational Speed	Worktable Velocity	Depth of Cut	Water Flow
1500 rpm	10 mm/s	3 mm	1 L/min

Each grinding slot or groove took 18 s to be made. A total of 32 grinding slots were made in each stone tile, i.e., 16 in each side of the tile (see Figure 8), and 7 tiles were used for evaluating each diamond tool. Therefore, the grinding tests comprised the removal of a considerable amount of granite (approximately 6.4 kg of granite per tool). Nonetheless, prior to the tests the tools were sharpened till stable cutting conditions were attained. The sharpening and conditioning procedure was conducted by observing the evolution of the segment's contact surface.

Figure 8. Sixteen grinding slots or grooves in one side of an Azul Alpalhão granite tile.

3. Results

3.1. Physical-Mechanical Properties of the Metallic Binders

The results of apparent density determined in the different binders are summarized in Table 5. The corresponding values of porosity (also indicated in Table 5) were calculated from the equation:

$$\% \text{ porosity} = \left(1 - \frac{\rho_a}{\rho_t}\right) \times 100\% , \tag{7}$$

where ρ_a represents the apparent density and ρ_t is the theoretical density (indicated in Table 2).

Table 5. Mean values (±standard deviation) of apparent density and porosity.

Property	Cobalite HDR	Cobalite HDR + 20% Cu	Cobalite HDR + 20% Fe	Next 300	Next 300 + 20% Cu	Next 300 + 20% Fe
Apparent density (g/cm³)	7.97 ± 0.05	8.16 ± 0.03	7.91 ± 0.02	7.78 ± 0.05	8.10 ± 0.02	7.80 ± 0.06
Porosity (%)	2.6 ± 0.6	2.2 ± 0.4	2.6 ± 0.3	4.2 ± 0.6	2.3 ± 0.2	3.3 ± 0.8

Figure 9a gives a graphical comparison of values of apparent density and values of theoretical density, whereas Figure 9b shows the values of porosity.

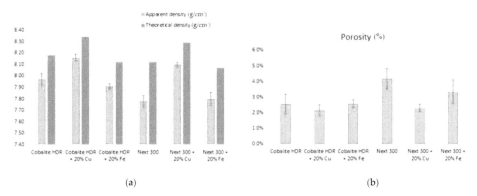

(a)   (b)

Figure 9. (a) Comparison of values of apparent and theoretical density; (b) values of porosity.

The results characterising the mechanical behaviour, obtained from Vickers hardness tests, resonance frequency analyses, and stress–strain curves from tensile tests, are summarized in Table 6 and plotted in the graphs presented in Figure 10.

Table 6. Mean values (±standard deviation) of mechanical properties.

	Cobalite HDR	Cobalite HDR + 20% Cu	Cobalite HDR + 20% Fe	Next 300	Next 300 + 20% Cu	Next 300 + 20% Fe
Vickers hardness (kg/mm²)	304 ± 5	251 ± 3	262 ± 4	233 ± 4	201 ± 6	221 ± 3
Young's modulus (GPa)	212 ± 3	185 ± 3	202 ± 3	214 ± 10	189 ± 4	208 ± 3
Yield strength (MPa)	1000 ± 15	750 ± 15	736 ± 22	612 ± 12	549 ± 33	531 ± 16
Rupture strength (MPa)	1012 ± 6	759 ± 12	747 ± 16	690 ± 24	663 ± 56	616 ± 9
Strain at rupture (%)	7.3 ± 0.8	3.2 ± 1.1	6.9 + 0.9	19.3 + 3.8	12.3 ± 4.1	21.0 ± 1.6
Toughness modulus (MJ/m³)	73 ± 8	24 ± 8	51 ± 7	125 ± 10	76 ± 12	120 ± 8

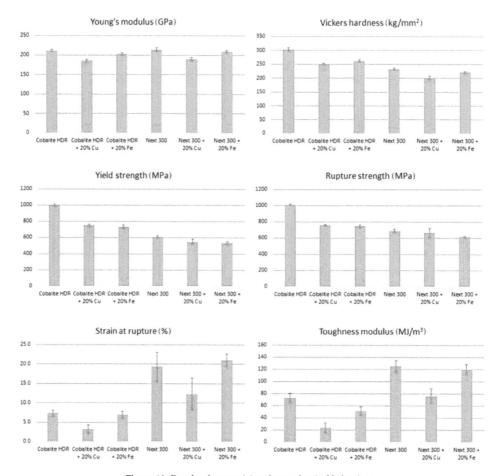

Figure 10. Results characterising the mechanical behaviour.

3.2. Comparison Between Two Diamond Tools

From the six different PM binders, we selected just two of them to produce the diamond tools in order to carry out grinding tests. The selection was made by applying Equation (1) and using the values the mechanical properties indicated therein (i.e., rupture strength, modulus of toughness, Vickers hardness, Young's modulus), which were determined experimentally for the six PM binders. The two PM binders/matrices showing the lowest values of matrix weight loss (Δm) were Cobalite HDR and Next 300.

Table 7 condenses the median values of F_r, Z, ϕ, and A obtained from tests carried out with the IST-Lisbon Classification Equipment applying the methodology described in Section 2.4.3.

Table 7. Comparison between the diamond tools with Cobalite HDR and Next 300.

Parameter	Cobalite HDR	Next 300
F_r (N)	195.9	218.2
Z (J/g)	483.8	488.5
ϕ (g/g)	384.3×10^{-6}	278.2×10^{-6}
A (J/g)	0.186	0.136

4. Discussion

After characterisation of the metallic binders, those that were considered the most suitable ones were used to produced grinding wheels geometrically equal but different in the type of metallic binder (using powders Cobalite HDR and Next 300). It is worth emphasising that the values shown in Table 7 are a consequence of long-term grinding tests, which comprised the removal of a considerable amount of granite (6.4 kg of granite per tool). The tests carried out on the two grinding wheels that were manufactured in this work showed that both of them are very efficient, and their wear rate is very low. For example, after removing 6.4 kilograms of granite, the grinding wheel with Cobalite HDR segments only lost 2.5 grams (i.e., 6400 g × 384.3 × 10^{-6} g/g) and reduction in tool diameter during the grinding test was practically unnoticeable, with ϕ-values determined by measuring differences in the weight of the tool.

From the results presented in Table 7 one can observe that the difference in Z-values shown by Cobalite HDR and Next 300 segments were very small. The grinding wheels composed by segments made of Cobalite HDR generated lower force (F_r) and even showed a slightly lower electric energy consumption per unit mass of removed stone (Z) in comparison to the grinding wheels made with Next 300 segments. On the contrary, Cobalite HDR segments showed much higher values of ϕ, i.e., mass loss of the tool per unit mass of removed stone. The conjunction of these different trends meant that the relative abrasiveness (parameter A) of Azul Alpalhão granite became higher when Cobalite HDR segments were employed.

The performance of the grinding wheels can be related to the mechanical properties of the metallic binders. Cobalite HDR segments (which generated lower contact force F_r) showed higher values of rupture strength, yield strength, and Vickers hardness, but lower values of toughness and strain at rupture. Metallic binders showing better diamond retention capacity and lower wear are supposed to be those with sufficient toughness. After the grinding tests, the segments were analysed by optical microscopy (see some photos in Figure 11) and from such inspection some conclusions were drawn. Diamonds with dark colour in the photos are those that were not yet active in the cutting process. Some diamonds only become totally active when they fracture. The tails in the metallic matrix have an important role in the process because they support the diamond when it cuts the stone. It is worth noting that the photos of Cobalite HDR segments are globally more yellowish compared to Next 300 segments, which means that Cobalite HDR segments had more active diamonds. This conclusion was confirmed by other type of observations, in which replicas of the segment surface were obtained and then analysed at the microscope. There was a higher concentration of active diamonds at the Cobalite HDR segments.

The grinding tests were conducted by imposing the depth of cut (3 mm in a single run) and, in our opinion, the complexity of the wear mechanism (involving multiple contact points between granite constituents, diamond particles, and metallic matrix) can only be adequately assessed if based on experimental evidence rather than on theoretical models. It is also important to consider the influence of the type of granite that is being cut. Since the resultant forces were higher in Next 300 segments (where a lower concentration of active diamonds was observed compared to the Cobalite HDR segments), it can be concluded that a higher concentration of active diamonds generates lower force during the cutting process. Previous studies conducted with different tools and different stone materials [17,18] have shown that the electric energy consumption varies linearly with the resultant force F_r. In the present study, lower average force F_r in the Cobalite HDR segments was accompanied by a slightly lower value of Z (see Table 7).

In fact, an earlier investigation [19] confirmed the abovementioned rationale, i.e., a higher concentration of active diamonds promotes lower forces and vice-versa. One of the objectives of that earlier study [19] consisted of comparing the forces generated when a totally new segment, without active diamonds, starts to be used, with the forces generated by a similar segment that was already used and had many active diamonds.

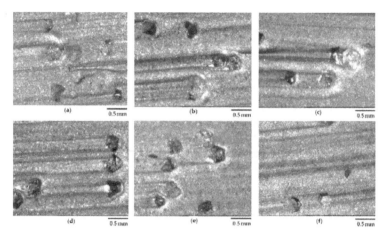

Figure 11. Examples of optical observations of the surface of the segments after the tests: (**a–c**) Cobalite HDR; (**d–f**) Next 300.

5. Conclusions

First of all, this work demonstrated a methodology to measure several mechanical properties of a series of isolated (i.e., without diamonds) PM matrix alloys in order to compare them. Then, it was necessary to associate those properties with the behaviour of the diamond tools when they were grinding one specific ornamental stone, using specific working parameters.

After characterisation of the metallic binders, those that were considered the most suitable ones were used to produced grinding wheels geometrically equal but different in the type of metallic binder (using powders Cobalite HDR and Next 300). It was then possible to realise that the metallic binder properties had a very important role in the diamond tool performance during the cutting process. Analysing the results, it was shown that the hardest metallic binder (Cobalite HDR) presented higher wear (compared to Next 300), when grinding Azul Alpalhão granite, under the specific working parameters.

The Next 300 metallic binder possessed a great value of toughness when compared to the other binders that were used in this work. Because of that, for grinding this type of granite, the binder Next 300 revealed a better diamond retention capacity, and at the same time showed higher deformation capacity (can absorb more energy prior to rupture). So, the diamond tool made with segments of Next 300 was more efficient (showed a lower wear rate) for the specific grinding process under consideration.

Author Contributions: C.A.A. and P.M.A. methodology, investigation, data curation, original draft preparation; J.C.F. formal analysis and validation; L.G.R. methodology, writing—review and editing; administration and funding acquisition.

Funding: This work was supported by Fundação para a Ciência e a Tecnologia (FCT), Portugal, through IDMEC—Instituto de Engenharia Mecânica (Pólo IST), under LAETA—Associated Laboratory for Energy, Transports and Aeronautics (project grant UID/EMS/50022/2019).

Conflicts of Interest: The authors declare no conflict of interest.

References

1. Rosa, L.G.; Fernandes, J.C.; Amaral, P.M. A Method for Classification of Stone Materials according to their Abrasiveness. In Proceedings of the EUROTHEN98 Workshop, Athens, Greece, 12–14 January 1998; pp. 338–345.
2. Rosa, L.G. Diamond tool characterisation methodologies: New perspectives for stone processing. In *Application of Diamond Technology in the Stone Sector*; Chapter 5; OSNET Editions; EUR 20637/4; Carosio, S., Paspaliaris, I., Eds.; European Commission: Brussels, Belgium, 2004; Volume 4, pp. 45–63.

3. Konstanty, J.S. Applications of powder metallurgy to cutting tools. In *Advances in Powder Metallurgy. Properties, Processing and Applications*; Chang, I., Zhao, Y., Eds.; Woodhead Publishing: Sawston, UK; Cambridge, UK, 2013; pp. 555–585.

4. Zhao, X.; Duan, L. A review of the diamond retention capacity of metal bond matrices. *Metals* **2018**, *8*, 307. [CrossRef]

5. Reis, L.; Amaral, P.M.; Li, B.; de Freitas, M.; Rosa, L.G. Evaluation of the residual stresses due to the sintering process of diamond–metal matrix hot-pressed tools. *Theor. Appl. Fract. Mech.* **2008**, *49*, 226–231. [CrossRef]

6. Li, B.; Amaral, P.M.; Reis, L.; Anjinho, C.A.; Rosa, L.G.; de Freitas, M. 3D-modelling of the local plastic deformation and residual stresses of PM diamond–metal matrix composites. *Comput. Mater. Sci.* **2010**, *47*, 1023–1030. [CrossRef]

7. Borowiecka-Jamrozek, J.; Lachowski, J. An analysis of the retention of a diamond particle in a metallic matrix after hot pressing. *Arch. Foundry Eng.* **2017**, *17*, 17–20. [CrossRef]

8. Borowiecka-Jamrozek, J.; Lachowski, J. The effect of the properties of the metal matrix on the retention of a diamond particle. *Metalurgija* **2017**, *56*, 83–86.

9. Xu, J.; Sheikh, A.H.; Xu, C. 3-D Finite element modelling of diamond pull-out failure in impregnateddiamond bits. *Diamond Relat. Mater.* **2017**, *71*, 1–12. [CrossRef]

10. Amaral, P.M.; Fernandes, J.C.; Rosa, L.G. Wear mechanisms in materials with granitic textures—Applicability of a lateral crack system model. *Wear* **2009**, *266*, 753–764. [CrossRef]

11. Yan, G.; Yue, W.; Meng, D.Z.; Lin, F.; Wu, Z.Y.; Wang, C.B. Wear performances and mechanisms of ultrahard polycrystalline diamond composite material grinded against granite. *Int. J. Refract. Met. Hard Mater.* **2016**, *54*, 46–53. [CrossRef]

12. Coelho, A. Avaliação do desgaste em matrizes metálicas usadas em ferramentas diamantadas e sua relação com as propriedades mecânicas. Master's Thesis, Universidade Técnica de Lisboa—Instituto Superior Técnico, Lisbon, Portugal, 2008.

13. Rosa, L.G.; Coelho, A.; Amaral, P.M.; Fernandes, J.C. Test methodology to evaluate the wear performance of PM matrices used in diamond impregnated tools for cutting hard materials. In *Powder Metallurgy for Automotive and High Performance Materials in Engineering Industries*; Ramakrishnan, P., Ed.; New Age International (P) Ltd.: New Delhi, India, 2012; pp. 186–193.

14. Clark, I.E.; Kamphuis, B.J. Cobalite HDR: A new prealloyed matrix powder for diamond construction tools. *IDR. Ind. Diamond Rev.* **2002**, *62*, 177–182.

15. Ugues, D.; Actis Grande, M.; Rosso, M. Study of the relation between hardness, toughness and resistance to wet abrasion in diamond segments. In Proceedings of the Euro PM2003, Valencia, Spain, 20–22 October 2003; pp. 375–383.

16. De Oliveira, H.C.P.; Coelho, A.; Amaral, P.M.; Fernandes, J.C.; Rosa, L.G. Comparison between cobalt and niobium as a matrix component for diamond impregnated tools used for stone cutting. *Key Eng. Mater.* **2013**, *548*, 98–105. [CrossRef]

17. Rosa, L.G.; Amaral, P.M.; Anjinho, C.A.; Fernandes, J.C. Evaluation of diamond tool behaviour for cutting stone materials. *Ind. Diamond Rev.* **2004**, *1*, 45–50.

18. Rosa, L.G.; Fernandes, J.C.; Anjinho, C.A.; Coelho, A.; Amaral, P.M. Long-term performance of stone-cutting tools. *Int. J. Refract. Met. Hard Mater.* **2015**, *49*, 276–282. [CrossRef]

19. Anjinho, C.A. Análise de ferramentas diamantadas utilizadas em corte e desbaste de mármores e granitos. Master's Thesis, Universidade Técnica de Lisboa—Instituto Superior Técnico, Lisbon, Portugal, 2004.

Article

Amorphous Al-Ti Powders Prepared by Mechanical Alloying and Consolidated by Electrical Resistance Sintering

Petr Urban [1], Fátima Ternero [2], Eduardo S. Caballero [2], Sooraj Nandyala [3], Juan Manuel Montes [2] and Francisco G. Cuevas [4,*]

[1] Department of Materials and Transportation Engineering and Science, Escuela Politécnica Superior, Universidad de Sevilla, 41011 Sevilla, Spain; purban@us.es
[2] Department of Materials and Transportation Engineering and Science, Escuela Técnica Superior de Ingeniería, Universidad de Sevilla, 41092 Sevilla, Spain; fternero@us.es (F.T.); esanchez3@us.es (E.S.C.); jmontes@us.es (J.M.M.)
[3] School of Metallurgy and Materials, College of Engineering and Physical Sciences, University of Birmingham, Birmingham B15 2TT, UK; s.h.nandyala@bham.ac.uk
[4] Department of Chemical Engineering, Physical Chemistry and Materials Science, Escuela Técnica Superior de Ingeniería, Universidad de Huelva, 21071 Huelva, Spain
* Correspondence: fgcuevas@dqcm.uhu.es; Tel.: +34-959-217-448

Received: 5 October 2019; Accepted: 22 October 2019; Published: 24 October 2019

Abstract: A novel processing method for amorphous $Al_{50}Ti_{50}$ alloy, obtained by mechanical alloying and subsequently consolidated by electrical resistance sintering, has been investigated. The characterisation of the powders and the confirmation of the presence of amorphous phase have been carried out by laser diffraction, scanning electron microscopy, X-ray diffraction, differential scanning calorimetry and transmission electron microscopy. The amorphous $Al_{50}Ti_{50}$ powders, milled for 75 h, have a high hardness and small plastic deformation capacity, not being possible to achieve green compacts for conventional sintering. Moreover, conventional sintering takes a long time, being not possible to avoid crystallisation. Amorphous powders have been consolidated by electrical resistance sintering. Electrically sintered compacts with different current intensities (7–8 kA) and processing times (0.8–1.6 s) show a porosity between 16.5 and 20%. The highest Vickers hardness of 662 HV is reached in the centre of an electrically sintered compact with 8 kA and 1.2 s from amorphous $Al_{50}Ti_{50}$ powder. The hardness results are compared with the values found in the literature.

Keywords: electrical resistance sintering; amorphisation; crystallisation; mechanical alloying; Al-Ti powders; porosity; hardness

1. Introduction

Al-Ti crystalline alloys are very attractive low-density materials with excellent properties at high temperatures [1]. Titanium aluminides are used for engine and airframe applications, mostly in the aerospace industry. The development of Al-Ti alloys began about 1970; however the alloys have only been used in these applications since about 2000 [2].

In general, the transformation of the crystalline phase of metallic materials to an amorphous phase can improve properties such as corrosion resistance [3], hardness [4] or mechanical strength [5]. An ideal method to obtain the amorphous phase in significant quantities is mechanical alloying.

Mechanical alloying (MA) is a peculiar grinding process that employs a high-energy ball mill in order to produce a composite metal powder with a controlled microstructure. This happens through repeated welding and fracturing of a mixture of metallic (and non-metallic) powders by the action of the mill balls. To achieve the desired amorphous phase, the optimisation of a considerable number of variables is required. Some of the important parameters affecting the amorphisation of the powders, without being completely independent, are the type of mill, the container and the milling balls, the rotating speed (intensity), the milling time and temperature. Moreover, the ratio of the weight of the balls and weight of the powder (RBP), the milling atmosphere, the process control agent (PCA), etc. also affect the final microstructure.

The obtained amorphous structure is thermodynamically instable, and in order to preserve the amorphous character of the alloyed powder, it is very convenient to have a fast consolidation technique in relation to diffusive processes, such as the known as Field Assisted Sintering Techniques (FAST) [6,7]. These techniques take advantage of the Joule heat generated by the passage of an electric current through the powder mass. One of these techniques, Spark Plasma Sintering (SPS), has recently been applied to mechanically alloyed $Al_{86}Ni_8Y_6$ amorphous powders [8,9] reaching temperatures of up to 400 °C for a relatively long time in the order of minutes. However, other techniques such as Electrical Resistance Sintering (ERS) need a much shorter heating period.

The sintering of crystalline metal powders using electricity has been known for several decades. Bloxam [10] was the first who reported and patented an electrical sintering method by applying a high intensity current through the metallic powder (electrical conductor); later, Weintraub and Rush [11] combined electric current with pressure, and Taylor [12] added the use of capacitors to eliminate the oxides covering the metal powders. These techniques are a type of hot pressing in which the powder itself generates heat due to the Joule effect, and are called "electrical resistance sintering under pressure". However, these methods are still today of great interest [13,14], coexisting with the traditional powder metallurgy (PM) route of cold pressing and furnace sintering. The main advantages are the achievement of very high densities with moderate or low pressures (around 100 MPa), the need of extraordinarily short sintering times (about one second) and the option of sintering in air. Its main disadvantage arises from operational difficulties, and the fact of not achieving a homogeneous distribution of temperature and densification in the powder mass.

In this work, amorphous $Al_{50}Ti_{50}$ alloy is prepared by MA and the effect of different parameters of the ERS process on porosity, microstructure, formation of intermetallic compounds, kinetics of devitrification and hardening are analysed.

2. Materials and Methods

Pure elemental powders of aluminum AS61 (Eckart-Werke, Eckart, Germany, purity > 99.5%) and titanium Se-Jong 4 (Se-Jong Materials, Incheon, South Korea, purity > 99.5%) were mixed to give the desired compositions of $Al_{50}Ti_{50}$. The manufacturer's chemical analysis for pure aluminum and pure titanium powders is given in Tables 1 and 2, respectively.

Table 1. Chemical analysis of Al AS61 powder as indicated by Eckart-Werke.

Element	Al	Si	Fe	Zn	Cu	Ti	Others
wt. %	>99.5	<0.250	<0.350	<0.050	<0.020	<0.020	<0.500

Table 2. Chemical analysis of Ti Se-Jong 4 powder as indicated by Se-Jong Materials.

Element	Ti	O	N	H	Fe	Si	Others
wt. %	>99.5	<0.440	<0.014	<0.010	<0.040	<0.080	<0.005 Mg <0.006 Mn

The mixture of 72 g of $Al_{50}Ti_{50}$ powder was placed in a sealed cylindrical 304 stainless steel vial, together with 304 stainless steel balls and 1.5 wt. % of ethylene bis-stearamide (EBS) wax ($C_{38}H_{76}N_2O_2$), as shown in Figure 1. The wax (PCA) function is to equilibrate the particles welding and rupture processes. Powders were alloyed up to 75 h in a high-energy attritor ball mill under a purified argon atmosphere to minimize contamination (oxygen and nitrogen from air). The RBP was fixed to 50:1, the rotor speed was 500 rpm, and the dry ball mill was carried out at room temperature. The MA experiment was interrupted at desired intervals and small amounts of the alloyed mix were taken out from the vial for analysis.

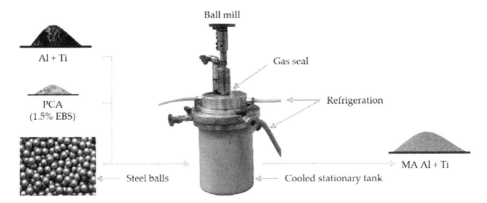

Figure 1. Scheme of the amorphisation procedure by mechanical alloying.

Size distribution and granulometric curves of the powders alloyed for different times were obtained by laser diffraction (Mastersizer 2000, Malvern Instruments, Malvern, UK). The structure and amorphisation progress of the ball milled powders were characterized by X-ray diffraction (XRD, D500, Siemens, Munich, Germany) with CuKα radiation, scanning electron microscopy (SEM, XL 30, Philips, Amsterdam, The Netherlands) and transmission electron microscopy (TEM, CM-200, Philips, Amsterdam, The Netherlands). The crystallisation process was followed by differential scanning calorimeter (DSC, Q100, TA Instruments, New Castle, DE, USA) under an argon gas flow. All the DSC results were obtained with heating rates of 40 °C/min up to a maximum temperature of 600 °C.

For the ERS process a resistance welding machine has been used (Serra Soldadura S.A., Barcelona, Spain), which provides the necessary electrical (high intensity and low voltage) and mechanical (load for compression) requirements. This adapted equipment produces the current with a one-phase transformer of 100 kVA, and the uniaxial load with a pneumatic cylinder reaching up to 14 kN. Moreover, the direct current intensity during the process is electronically controlled, and follow-up sensors record the outstanding parameters as the mobile punch displacement, the load and the effective voltage and current intensity.

Once milled, powders were processed to obtain a bulk material. The 12 mm in diameter ceramic die (Figure 2) was confined by a metallic hoop. The outlets of the die were closed with water cooled electrodes of temperature resistant copper (98.9%Cu–1%Cr–0.1%Zr), and electro-erosion resistant wafers (75.3%W–24.6%Cu) in direct contact with the powder. The amorphous powders (2 g) were placed between the wafers for sintering. Due to their low thermal conductivity, the wafers dump the heat flow from the powder mass to the electrodes.

Powders were consolidated with a compaction pressure of 80 MPa and only one electric pulse for each specimen. Several current intensities (7.0, 7.5 and 8.0 kA) and current passing times (40 to 80 cycles, with 50 cycles = 1.0 s) were tested.

Hardness tests and light micrographs were carried out on diametrical planes of the cylindrical compacts mounted in Bakelite resin. Hardness measurements distribution in the diametrical plane is shown in Figure 3. (Indentations were carried out in different positions due to the non-uniform porosity distribution, coming from the temperature gradient generated during consolidation). Indentations were carried out in the center (HV_c), in the outer layer near the surface (HV_o) and in the inner area (HV_i) of the compact. The hardness results were compared with the values of other investigations using different sintering techniques.

The structure and crystallisation progress of the compacts consolidated by ERS were characterized by XRD.

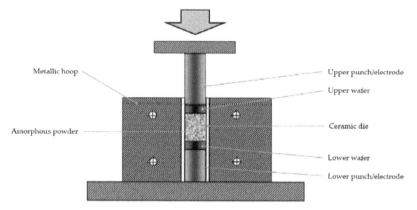

Figure 2. Scheme of the die, electrodes and powders in the ERS experiments. The upper punch/electrode and upper wafer are the only parts with movement allowed.

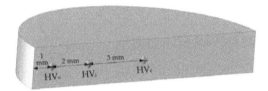

Figure 3. Positions of hardness indentations on a diametrical section of the cut specimen. Hardness in the other half is known because of the compact symmetry.

3. Results

3.1. Amorphisation

In the first part of the investigation, amorphous and/or nanocrystalline powders of the Al-Ti alloy are prepared by MA. The characterisation of the powders is done for different milling times. Laser diffraction measures particles size, SEM reveals morphology and confirms particle sizes. XRD indicates whether an amorphous and/or nanocrystalline phase is present and identifies the different crystalline phases. DSC shows the crystallisation temperature of the amorphous phase and TEM identifies amorphous, nanocrystalline and/or crystalline phases.

3.1.1. Laser Diffraction

At the beginning of the milling process, aluminium powder has an average particle size d (0.5) of about 71.2 μm, and titanium powder of about 29.6 μm. As shown in Figure 4, the mixture of the two pure metals, in the 50/50 atomic ratio, results in an average particle size of about 41.3 μm.

During the first hours of milling, when fracture processes predominate, the average particle size decreases considerably, reaching about 18.5 μm for 5 h. Between 5 and 25 h, the particle size remains stable without significant changes. However, going further of 25 h of milling, the dislocations density in the powder increases considerably, hardening it enough to make particle size to decrease to minimum values. Finally, it remains stable up to 75 h, with d (0.5) values for 50 and 75 h of 10.4 and 8.6 μm, respectively.

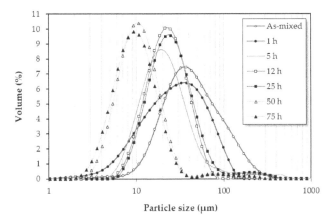

Figure 4. Granulometric curves of $Al_{50}Ti_{50}$ mixture and MA powders for different milling times.

3.1.2. Scanning Electron Microscopy

Figure 5a shows the mixed powders prior to ball milling, with irregular shaped large particles of aluminium and smaller and more equiaxial ones of titanium. In the initial phase of milling (up to 1 h), the powder particles of Al and Ti are flattened and fragmented by ball-powder-ball collisions. After this time, particles of Al and Ti can still be distinguished with irregular shapes. After 5 h (Figure 5b), particles are more round and reach a quite small particle size of about 20 μm. The homogenisation by solid solution results clear. Between 5 and 12 h, the particles have a very irregular rounded shape (Figure 5c). When milling continues (25–75 h), particles are refined to about 10 μm, showing an almost spherical shape (Figure 5d).

Figure 5. SEM micrographs of (**a**) the Al and Ti powders mixture, and the $Al_{50}Ti_{50}$ alloy milled for (**b**) 5, (**c**) 12 and (**d**) 75 h.

3.1.3. X-ray Diffraction

The initial study of the milled powders has been completed by XRD analysis (Figure 6). It is observed that for the first 5 h of milling, the intensity of the diffraction peaks of Al and Ti decreases as time increases. At the same time, the width of the peaks increases considerably as a result of the decrease in crystallite size. After 12 h of milling, the formation of a nanocrystalline/amorphous phase begins by atomic diffusion between Al and Ti. Thus, after 25 h, independent peaks of Al and Ti cannot at all be observed and a characteristic wide peak of the amorphous phases appears with the maximum around $2\Theta = 39°$. The percentage of amorphous phase increases with milling time, as evidenced by the widening of the halo.

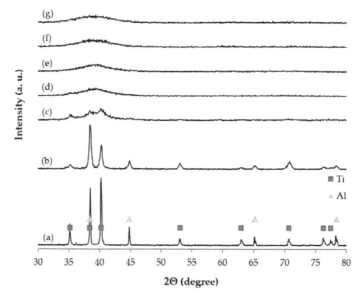

Figure 6. XRD patterns of (**a**) the Al and Ti powders mixture, and powders milled for (**b**) 1, (**c**) 5, (**d**) 12, (**e**) 25, (**f**) 50 and (**g**) 75 h.

3.1.4. Differential Scanning Calorimetry

Amorphisation can also be verified by using DSC (Figure 7). For the powder milled for 12 and 25 h, the appearance of an exothermic peak from 500 °C is observed, probably corresponding to the nanocrystals growth, and partial crystallisation of the amorphous phase formed during MA. After 50 h, with a powder completely amorphous, there is a change in the shape of the curves obtained. An endothermic peak appears at about 400–550 °C, possibly reflecting the heat flow anomaly characteristic of the glass transition (difficult to find for lower milling times because of the lower amount of amorphous phase). This endothermic peak could hide the exothermic peak corresponding to the crystallisation of the amorphous phase, or maybe crystallization is retarded to higher temperatures, forming titanium aluminides (AlTi, Al_3Ti and $AlTi_3$), which again must take place above 500 °C. According to these results, in order to maintain the amorphous structure these powders could have a maximum temperature for consolidation, using conventional techniques, bellow 500 °C.

3.1.5. Transmission Electron Microscopy

In order to confirm the presence of the amorphous phase, TEM of milled powders for 5, 25 and 75 h is shown in Figure 8. A crystalline/nanocrystalline structure can be found for 5 h of milling. After

25 h of milling possible amorphous zones can be found in the sample together with a nanocrystalline structure. However, after 75 h of milling, the crystalline phase has totally disappeared of the material.

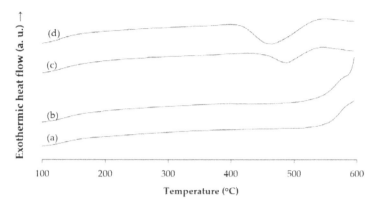

Figure 7. DSC of powders milled for (a) 12, (b) 25, (c) 50 and (d) 75 h.

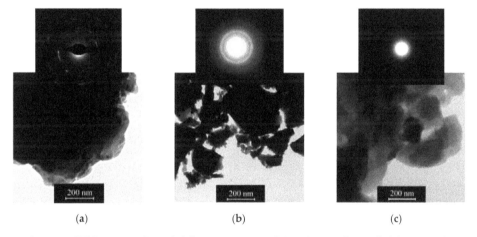

(a)   (b)   (c)

Figure 8. TEM micrographs and diffraction patterns of the $Al_{50}Ti_{50}$ alloy milled for (a) 5, (b) 25 and (c) 75 h, showing (a) crystalline and nanocrystalline phase, (b) nanocrystalline phase and (c) amorphous phase.

3.1.6. X-ray Diffraction after Heat Treatment

The study of the milled powders for 75 h has been completed with XRD analyses after heating at various temperatures. Samples have been heated to 300, 500, 650 and 850 °C at 10 °C/min and maintained at temperature for 1 h, and after cooling, XRD have been performed at room temperature. As expected, up to 300 °C (Figure 9a,b) XRD does not show any significant structural change and no evidence of crystallisation is found. Between 500 and 650 °C (Figure 9c,d) the amorphous phase begins to crystallise giving rise to titanium aluminides such as AlTi, Al_3Ti and $AlTi_3$ (Figure 9d), although the presence of Al crystals is also possible. This transformation of the amorphous to the crystalline phase can be confirmed in the diffraction pattern at 850 °C (Figure 9e), where all the main peaks are already well differentiated from each other.

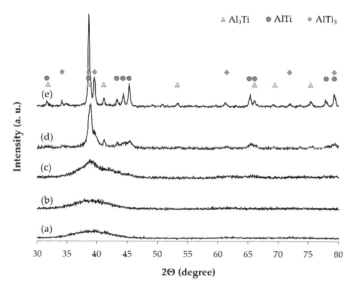

Figure 9. Room temperature XRD patterns of (**a**) the $Al_{50}Ti_{50}$ alloy milled for 75 h, and heated to (**b**) 300, (**c**) 500, (**d**) 650 and (**e**) 850 °C, after cooling.

3.2. Electrical Resistance Sintering

3.2.1. Porosity

At the beginning of the ERS process (pressing stage, at 80 MPa), the powder mass porosity decreases very little, both because of the high hardness of the amorphous powders and the low applied pressure. In general, after the whole process, amorphous powders milled for 75 h and ERS with low intensity still have a high porosity (Figure 10). For higher current intensities, the densification capacity increases. The increase in processing time (in cycles in Figure 10) acts in similar way.

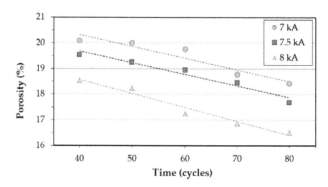

Figure 10. Final porosity vs. sintering time (50 cycles = 1 s) of $Al_{50}Ti_{50}$ ERS compacts (from powder milled for 75 h) for different current intensities.

No satisfactory experiments were carried out with current intensities lower than 7 kA or higher than 8 kA. For low current intensities, the high electrical resistivity of the powder mass makes sintering difficult. For high current intensities, sintered compacts stick and cannot be separated of the wafers. As expected, it results difficult to remove the porosity of hardened amorphous powders after MA, however, this is not the case for softer unmilled crystalline powders. The porosity of ERS compacts made from pure Ti powders is much lower and can reach values of up to 4% even with lower current intensities (Figure 11).

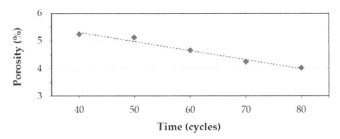

Figure 11. Final porosity vs. sintering time (50 cycles = 1 s) of pure Ti ERS compacts (from unmilled powder) for 6 kA.

As observed in the trend lines in Figures 10 and 11, the slope for pure Ti compacts is smaller than in the case of milled $Al_{50}Ti_{50}$ compacts. Therefore, for ductile powders, the increase in sintering time does not affect the decrease in porosity as much as in the case of very hard powders.

The high-porosity ERS 7/40 Al-Ti compact (sintered with intensity of 7 kA and 40 cycles) has been selected to show the effect of ERS on the microstructure (Figure 12). The uniform porosity distribution generally found in conventionally sintered compacts differs from the non-uniform distribution after ERS. Electrically sintered compacts have a more porous outer layer with a width of about 2 mm (Figure 12a,c) and a densified centre (Figure 12b,d). The ERS 7/40 compact has an average porosity of about 20.1%, however, the porosity in the outer layer is about 32.8% and in the centre about 8.5%. The porosity variation is caused by the unequal temperature distribution in the compact, consequence of the preferential electric paths inside the compact and the heat sink through the die walls. Temperature rises less and decreases faster near the wall of the ceramic die.

3.2.2. X-ray Diffraction of Compacts after Heat Treatment

An additional and important issue to consider is the effect of the sintering process on the microstructure. Although the sintering process is very quick, the temperature variation inside the compact could affect, as shown next, the stability of the amorphous phase. Also, the effect of additional exposure to high temperatures on the microstructure is of interest, because of the typical use of Al-Ti alloys [1].

The amorphous phase stability with temperature in the ERS 7/40 compact has been evaluated by XRD carried out at different temperatures (Figure 13). At room temperature (Figure 13a), after the ERS process, a small wide peak appears, due to the partial transformation of the amorphous phase into nanocrystals. Nanocrystals could probably be of Al, or some of the intermetallic compounds AlTi, Al_3Ti and $AlTi_3$. If the compact is heated to 300 °C (Figure 13b), the main peak (at 39°) starts growing, as a result of the increase of the crystalline phase. The peak still shows a significant width, typical of a small crystallite size. Although the temperature is not very high, the effect of time at this temperature (heating rate of 10 °C/min and 0.5 h at temperature) makes the amorphous structure to dissipate as compared with the sintered compact. At higher temperatures of 500 and 650 °C (Figure 13c,d) there is not a big difference between the main peaks, resulting a stable structure.

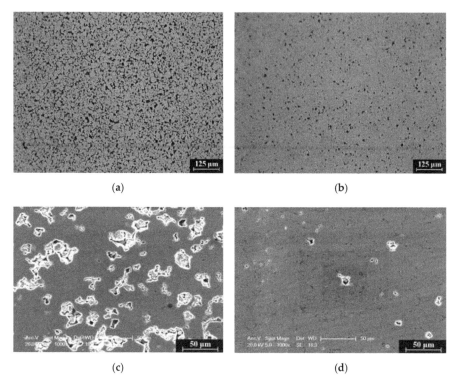

Figure 12. Distribution of porosity in the periphery (**a,c**) and core (**b,d**) of the ERS 7/40 compact observed by optical microscopy (**a,b**) and SEM (**c,d**).

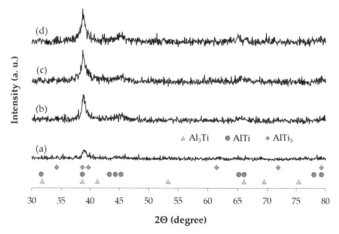

Figure 13. High temperature XRD patterns of ERS (7/40) $Al_{50}Ti_{50}$ compact heated up to (**a**) 25, (**b**) 300, (**c**) 500 and (**d**) 650 °C.

3.2.3. Hardness of Al-Ti Alloys

The difference between the hardness of $Al_{50}Ti_{50}$ ERS compacts and that of other ones mentioned in the literature, prepared with similar procedures, has been studied. The hardness of the compacts, in general, depends mainly on two factors: the hardness of the powders that constitute the compact and the density of the resulting compact. Figure 14 shows the hardness values of some materials related to those studies.

First, the hardness values of the starting materials should be highlighted. Pure aluminium and titanium have a very low hardness compared to their alloys. Pure aluminium powder has a hardness of only 20 HV [15]. This low hardness of the aluminium powder can be increased by mechanical alloying, both because of the grains refinement and by the effect of the PCA, leading to the formation of a solid solution, thus increasing the hardness of the powder to 127 HV [16], which decreases after a short stress relieve treatment at 600 °C to 97 HV [16]. In addition, after conventional consolidation by uniaxial pressing and furnace sintering the hardness of pure aluminium can decrease to 80 HV [16], mainly because of the grain growth. It is also possible to increase the hardness of conventionally consolidated pure Al compacts to about 180 HV by milling the powder in an atmosphere of ammonia [17,18]. Apart from grain refining, ammonia causes the formation of nitrogen-rich compounds that produce dispersion hardening.

Pure titanium has a higher hardness than pure aluminium. Commercial powders can reach up to about 70 HV [15] or 160 HV [19]. This difference depends largely on the morphology and/or fabrication process of the powder. On the other hand, pure titanium compacts can reach 255 HV [20], 270 HV [21] and 290 HV [19].

In Al-Ti alloyed powder mixtures and compacts, there is a noticeable increase in hardness compared to pure Al. In general, a higher content of Ti produces a greater final hardness, because of forming an Al(Ti) solid solution after mechanical alloying and/or intermetallic compounds like Al_3Ti, AlTi and $AlTi_3$ after heat treating or sintering. For instance, with the presence of only 2.88 at.% of titanium, sintered aluminium compacts increase the hardness from 80 HV to about 104 HV [22]. With the increase of titanium up to 5.58 at.%, the hardness increases to about 202 HV [15]. In addition, for the $Al_{50}Ti_{50}$ alloy, the hardness increases to values between 300 and 790 HV [23–28].

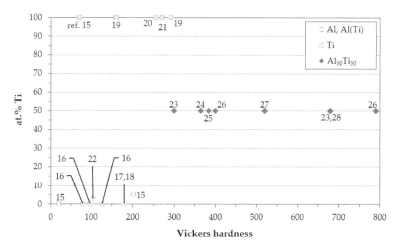

Figure 14. Hardness of aluminium, titanium and $Al_{50}Ti_{50}$ alloys according to bibliographic data [15–28].

The hardness results of the ERS compacts of this work are shown in Figure 15. Independently of the initial powder microstructure (crystalline or amorphous) current intensity has a similar effect on sintered compacts, with higher intensities resulting in higher hardness. However, the effect of sintering time does not have much influence on hardness, because the effect of time is lower on the energy transferred to the compact. In all the specimens, the centre (HV_c) has a greater hardness than the outer layer (HV_o). The hardness measured for the inner zone (HV_i) does not show much difference with the centre hardness, since the porosity gradient is not uniform. There is a wide area around the compact centre with low and homogeneous porosity. Between the denser inner and the outer area, there is a sharp porosity change.

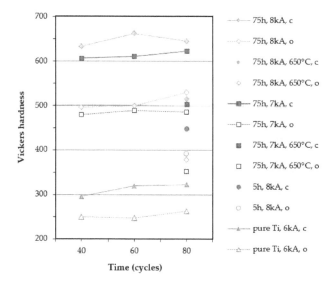

Figure 15. Hardness of ERS Al$_{50}$Ti$_{50}$ (and Ti for comparison) as-sintered and heat-treated compacts.

The highest measured hardness corresponds to the centre of the compact ERS at 8 kA from amorphous powder milled for 75 h. The microstructure contains mainly nanocrystals of aluminium and Al$_3$Ti, AlTi and AlTi$_3$ compounds with possible amorphous phase residues. Vickers hardness reaches values between 633 and 662 HV for different sintering times.

If lower current intensity (7 kA) is applied, the hardness in the compact centre decreases slightly to values between 607 and 623 HV because of the lower densification, although a higher amount of amorphous phase remains untransformed.

The hardness in the outer layer of the compact decreases considerably for both 8 kA and 7 kA. Hardness values vary between 480 and 530 HV. The prevalence of an amorphous structure in this area because of the lower attained temperature, versus a nanocrystalline or crystalline structure development, should account for a higher hardness. However, the predominant factor is the increase in porosity, negatively affecting hardness.

After an annealing heat treatment (for 7 and 8 kA ERS compact) up to 650 °C for 1 h, the hardness decreases considerably. In the centre, the hardness reaches 503–515 HV, with values between 352–378 HV in the outer porous layer. This decrease of around 20% is due to the amorphous/nanocrystalline to crystalline phase transformation and grain growth.

For ERS compacts prepared from Al-Ti powder milled for 5 h, the hardness reaches values between 392 and 448 HV in the inner and periphery, respectively. After 5 h of milling, the powder microstructure has not reached an amorphous structure, but a supersaturated solid solution with areas of aluminium and titanium. After ERS processing with 8 kA, the microstructure will probably consist in a small percentage of intermetallic compounds together with solid solutions and pure elements.

Finally, it has been confirmed that the hardness of the ERS 6/40–80 pure Ti compacts (both in the centre and periphery) is lower than that of the compacts prepared from milled Al$_{50}$Ti$_{50}$ powders. Hardness ranges between 248–263 HV for the outer layer and 296–323 HV for the centre of the compact. These compacts are highly densified, but no hardening mechanism is developed for pure titanium.

4. Conclusions

A novel method of compacts processing of the $Al_{50}Ti_{50}$ alloy obtained by mechanical alloying and subsequent consolidation by ERS has been investigated. As expected, amorphous and/or nanocrystalline, powders of the $Al_{50}Ti_{50}$ alloy were prepared by mechanical alloying up to 75 h. Particles size of the powders reached about 8.6 μm and showed an almost spherical shape. It has been checked that the amorphous phase crystallizes at about 500 °C, forming titanium aluminides.

Amorphous and/or nanocrystalline powders of the $Al_{50}Ti_{50}$ alloy were successfully sintered by ERS with different current intensities (7–8 kA) and processing times (0.8–1.6 s). This technique avoids the difficulty of obtaining a green compact for conventional sintering because of the high hardness of these compacts. Electrically sintered compacts show non-uniform distribution of porosity with a porous outer layer and densified centre. For instance, the ERS 7/40 compact has a global porosity of about 20.1%, however, the porosity in the outer layer is about 32.8% and in the centre about 8.5%. The electrically sintered compact processed with 8 kA for 1.2 s from amorphous powders reaches a significant Vickers hardness of up to 662 HV.

Author Contributions: Conceptualization, P.U., J.M.M. and F.G.C.; methodology, J.M.M. and F.G.C.; validation, P.U., F.T., E.S.C. and S.N.; writing—original draft, P.U.; writing—review & editing, P.U., F.T., E.S.C., S.N., J.M.M. and F.G.C.

Funding: This research was funded by Ministerio de Economía y Competitividad (Spain) and Feder (EU) through the research projects DPI2015-69550-C2-1-P and DPI2015-69550-C2-2-P.

Acknowledgments: The authors also wish to thank the technicians J. Pinto, M. Madrid and M. Sánchez (University of Seville, Spain) for experimental assistance.

Conflicts of Interest: The authors declare no conflict of interest.

References

1. Appel, F.; Clemens, H.; Fischer, F.D. Modeling concepts for intermetallic titanium aluminides. *Prog. Mater. Sci.* **2016**, *81*, 55–124. [CrossRef]

2. Appel, F.; Wagner, R. Intermetallics: Titanium aluminides. In *Encyclopedia of Materials: Science and Technology*, 2nd ed.; Elsevier Science & Technology: London, UK, 2001; pp. 4246–4264.

3. Xia, Z.H.; Zhang, M.; Zhang, Y.; Zhao, Y.; Liaw, P.K.; Qiao, J.W. Effects of Ni-P amorphous films on mechanical and corrosion properties of $Al_{0.3}CoCrFeNi$ high-entropy alloys. *Prog. Mater. Sci.* **2019**, *104*, 250–329.

4. Krasnowski, M.; Kulik, T. Nanocrystalline or amorphous matrix $Al_{60}Fe_{15}Ti_{15}(Co/Mg/Zr)_5–5\%B$ composites produced by consolidation of mechanically alloyed powders-lightweight materials with high hardness. *Intermetallics* **2012**, *28*, 120–127. [CrossRef]

5. Qiao, J.C.; Wang, Q.; Pelletier, J.M.; Kato, H.; Casalini, R.; Crespo, D.; Pineda, E.; Yao, Y.; Yang, Y. Structural heterogeneities and mechanical behavior of amorphous alloys. *Intermetallics* **2018**, *94*, 65–72. [CrossRef]

6. Olevsky, E.A.; Dudina, D.V. *Field-Assisted Sintering, Science and Applications*; Springer: Cham, Switzerland, 2018.

7. Olevsky, E.A. *Spark-Plasma Sintering and Related Field-Assisted Powder Consolidation Technologies*; MDPI Books: Basel, Switzerland, 2017.

8. Maurya, R.S.; Sahu, A.; Laha, T. Quantitative phase analysis in $Al_{86}Ni_8Y_6$ bulk glassy alloy synthesized by consolidating mechanically alloyed amorphous powder via spark plasma sintering. *Mater. Des.* **2016**, *93*, 96–103. [CrossRef]

9. Maurya, R.S.; Sahu, A.; Laha, T. Effect of consolidation pressure on phase evolution during sintering of mechanically alloyed Al86Ni8Y6 amorphous powders via spark plasma sintering. *Mater. Sci. Eng. A* **2016**, *649*, 48–56. [CrossRef]

10 Lux, J. For an Improved Manufacture of Electric Incandescent Lamp Filaments from Tungsten or Molybdenum or an Alloy Thereof. Great Britain Patent No. 27002, 13 December 1906.

11. Weintraub, G.; Rush, H. Process and Apparatus for Sintering Refractory Materials. U.S. Patent No. 1071488A, 26 August 1913.

12. Taylor, G.F. Apparatus for Making Hard Metal Compositions. U.S. Patent No. 1896854, 7 February 1933.

13. Gallardo, J.M.; Agote, I.; Astacio, R.; Schubert, T.; Cintas, J.; Montes, J.M.; Torres, Y.; Cuevas, F.G. Hard metal production by ERS: Processing parameters role in final properties. *Metals* **2019**, *9*, 172. [CrossRef]
14. Montes, J.M.; Gómez Cuevas, F.; Ternero, F.; Astacio, R.; Sánchez Caballero, E.; Cintas, J. Medium-frequency electrical resistance sintering of oxidized C.P. iron powder. *Metals* **2018**, *8*, 426. [CrossRef]
15. Cuevas, F.G.; Cintas, J.; Montes, J.M.; Gallardo, J.M. Al-Ti powder produced through mechanical alloying for different times. *J. Mater. Sci.* **2006**, *41*, 8339–8346. [CrossRef]
16. Cintas, J.; Rodríguez, J.A.; Gallardo, J.M.; Herrera, E.J. Simplification of the processing of milled aluminium powder and mechanical properties evaluation. *Rev. Metal.* **2001**, *37*, 370–375. [CrossRef]
17. Caballero, E.S.; Cintas, J.; Cuevas, F.G.; Montes, J.M.; Herrera-García, M. Improvement in the mechanical behavior of mechanically alloyed aluminum using short-time NH_3 flow. *Metall. Mater. Trans. A* **2016**, *47*, 6481–6486. [CrossRef]
18. Cintas, J.; Cuevas, F.G.; Montes, J.M.; Herrera, E.J. High-strength PM aluminium by milling in ammonia gas and sintering. *Scr. Mater.* **2005**, *53*, 1165–1170. [CrossRef]
19. Ohno, T.; Kubota, M. Effect of mechanical milling atmosphere on hardness and constituent phase of pure titanium. *J. Jpn. Inst. Light Met.* **2010**, *60*, 647–653. [CrossRef]
20. Kao, Y.L.; Tu, G.C.; Huang, C.A.; Liu, T.T. A study on the hardness variation of α- and β-pure titanium with different grain sizes. *Mater. Sci. Eng.* **2005**, *398*, 93–98. [CrossRef]
21. Poondla, N.; Srivatsan, T.S.; Patnaik, A.; Petraroli, M. A study of the microstructure and hardness of two titanium alloys: Commercially pure and Ti-6Al-4V. *J. Alloy. Compd.* **2009**, *486*, 162–167. [CrossRef]
22. Cuevas, F.G.; Cintas, J.; Rodríguez, J.A.; Gallardo, J.M. Structure and Properties of consolidated attrition-milled Al-5%Ti PM specimens. *Mater. Sci. Forum* **2003**, *426–432*, 4307–4312. [CrossRef]
23. Weisheit, A.; Mordike, B.L.; Smarsly, W.; Richter, K.H. Laser surface remelting and laser surface gas alloying of an intermetallic TiAl alloy. *Lasers Eng.* **2000**, *10*, 63–81.
24. Sahu, P. Lattice imperfections in intermetallic Ti-Al alloys: An X-ray diffraction study of the microstructure by the Rietveld method. *Intermetallics* **2006**, *14*, 180–188. [CrossRef]
25. Adams, A.G.; Rahaman, M.N.; Dutton, R.E. Microstructure of dense thin sheets of γ-TiAl fabricated by hot isostatic pressing of tape-cast monotapes. *Mater. Sci. Eng.* **2008**, *477*, 137–144. [CrossRef]
26. Itsukaichi, T.; Masuyama, K.; Umenoto, M.; Okane, I. Mechanical alloying of Al-Ti powder mixtures and their subsequent consolidation. *J. Mater. Res.* **1993**, *8*, 1817–1828. [CrossRef]
27. Takekazu, N.; Shigeoki, S.; Takashi, Y.; Masateru, N.; Masaru, Y. Preparation of functionally graded materials by pulse current pressure sintering of ball milled Al-50 at%Ti powder. *Mater. Trans. JIM* **2000**, *41*, 457–460.
28. Samsonov, G.V.; Vinnitsky, I.M. *Refractory Compounds, A Reference Book*, 2nd ed.; Metallurgiya: Moscow, Russia, 1976; pp. 300–307.

 *metals*

Article

Strategy to Enhance Magnetic Properties of $Fe_{78}Si_9B_{13}$ Amorphous Powder Cores in the Industrial Condition

Haibo Sun [1,*], Ce Wang [2], Weihong Chen [1] and Jiexin Lin [1]

[1] Department of Materials Science and Engineering, School of Materials Science and Energy Engineering, Foshan University, Foshan 528000, China; yfzx001@catech.cn (W.C.); LJXgrape@163.com (J.L.)
[2] Product R&D Center, China Amorphous Technology Co., Ltd., Foshan 528241, China; catech_js17@catech.cn
* Correspondence: sunmyseven@126.com; Tel.: +86-137-5152-0889

Received: 3 February 2019; Accepted: 23 March 2019; Published: 26 March 2019

Abstract: In this study, the soft magnetic properties of $Fe_{78}Si_9B_{13}$ amorphous magnetic powder cores (AMPCs) were enhanced by coordinately adjusting the technological parameters, including the particle size distribution, molding pressure, and coating agent content, in the industrial condition. The results show that the optimized comprehensive soft magnetic properties of the $Fe_{78}Si_9B_{13}$ AMPCs could be obtained under the following process conditions: (1) the distribution of particle size is 20 wt.% for 140–170 mesh, 70 wt.% for 170–270 mesh, and 10 wt.% for 270–400 mesh; (2) the molding pressure is in the range of 2.35–2.45 GPa; and (3) the additive amount of sodium silicate is 1.5 wt.%. After the collaborative optimization, the AMPCs' compact density, ρ, the effective permeability, μ_e, and the residual effective permeability at the applied magnetizing field of 7.96 kA/m, μ_e@7.96 kA/m, increased from 5.61 g/cm³ to 5.86 g/cm³, from 58.13 to 77.01, and from 40.36 to 49.57, respectively. The attenuation ratio of the effective permeability, when in the frequency band of 20–100 kHz, was less than 0.85%. The core loss at the 50 kHz for the maximum magnetic flux density of 0.1 T reduced from 380.85 mW/cm³ to 335.23 mW/cm³. This work will encourage the further application of Fe-based AMPCs in the fields of electronics and telecommunication.

Keywords: amorphous powders; amorphous magnetic powder cores; soft magnetic properties; permeability; direct current (DC) bias performance

---

1. Introduction

Magnetic powder cores (MPCs), consisting of ferromagnetic powders and electrical insulating materials formed by compacting [1], have been widely used in a range of electrical components, such as choking coils [2], inductors [3], transformers [3,4], filters [5], and so on [6]. Further developments to electronic devices are aimed at achieving a high frequency, miniaturization, and high application power. Following this trend, the supply of high effective permeability with a stabilized frequency characteristic, low core loss at a high frequency, and excellent direct current (DC) superposition performance by the MPCs, have become key issues.

Fe-based amorphous magnetic powder cores (AMPCs) with excellent soft magnetic properties, including high magnetic saturation, ultra-low core loss, and good DC-bias performance, have attracted lots of attention from different researchers [7–9]. Comparing to the traditional Sendust (FeSiAl) MPCs, the Fe-based AMPCs (such as $Fe_{78}Si_9B_{13}$) have a better DC superposition performance and a lower core loss [8,9]. To further improve the comprehensive soft magnetic properties of the Fe-based AMPCs, three main different aspects of works have been carried out as follows.

(1) The alloy composition design. Liu et al. [10] investigated the influence of Si addition on the glass forming ability for the $Fe_{77}P_6B_{14-x}Si_xNb_2Cr_1$ ($x = 0–4$) alloys. They pointed out that the $Fe_{77}P_6B_{10}Si_4Nb_2Cr_1$ AMPCs exhibited excellent magnetic properties, including high effective

permeability of 82, low core loss of 308 mW/cm^3 at 100 kHz under the maximum magnetic flux density (B_m) of 0.05 T, and superior DC-bias permeability of 62% at a bias field of 7.96 kA/m. Guo et al. [11] studied the magnetic properties of the (Fe$_{0.76}$Si$_{0.09}$B$_{0.1}$P$_{0.05}$)$_{99}$Nb$_1$ AMPCs. It was shown that the AMPCs possessed an effective permeability of 56, and a DC-bias permeability of 85% at an applied field of 7.96 kA/m. Li et al. [12] indicated that the Fe$_{76}$Si$_9$B$_{10}$P$_5$ AMPCs exhibited an effective permeability of 70, and a core loss of 1210 mW/cm^3 at 100 kHz for B_m = 0.1 T.

(2) The insulation material selection. It is necessary to improve the electrical resistivity of ferromagnetic powders by coating a suitable electrically insulating material for high-frequency applications of the MPCs [13]. Generally, the organic materials [14,15] of epoxy resin and phenol formaldehyde resin, and the inorganic materials, such as metal oxides [16,17] (e.g., SiO$_2$, MgO, and Al$_2$O$_3$) and phosphates [18] (e.g., FePO$_4$, and Zn$_3$ (PO$_4$)$_2$), were employed as the surface insulation coatings for the MPCs. Recently, to further improve the comprehensive soft magnetic properties of the MPCs, the surface-oxidized layer consisted of Fe$_2$O$_3$ and Fe$_3$O$_4$ [3,13] and the ferromagnetic materials with high resistivity (e.g., ferrites nanoparticles [12,19,20] and permalloy particles [21]) were proposed.

(3) Processing optimization. Yagi et al. [22] put forward the hot-pressing technique to enhance the comprehensive magnetic properties of the Fe-based AMPCs. Zheng et al. [23] evaluated the comprehensive magnetic properties of the Fe-based AMPCs with various orientations of the powder-flakes. It was shown that the powders parallel to the external magnetic field were beneficial for achieving the optimum magnetic performances of the AMPCs. Li et al. presented that the pre-annealing treatment for the powders [24], longitudinal [25] and transverse [26] magnetic field annealing can improve the effective permeability and reduce the core loss for the Fe-based AMPCs. Moreover, the influence of particle size, coating agent content on the AMPCs' magnetic properties was also separately investigated [12,27].

The literature above proved that the MPCs' comprehensive soft magnetic properties strongly depend on the fabrication processing parameters of the powder cores. Moreover, it is well-known that the effective permeability, the frequency characteristic, the core loss at high frequency, and the DC-bias property, are the MPCs' four key performance indexes that interact with each other, and respectively correspond to miniaturization, frequency band, rated power, and energy efficiency of the electronic devices. Consequently, the four performance indexes must be integrated and coordinated. In this paper, the soft magnetic properties of Fe$_{78}$Si$_9$B$_{13}$ AMPCs were optimized by coordinately adjusting the technological parameters, including the particle size distribution, molding pressure, and coating agent content, in the industrial condition. A package of optimized fabricating parameters for the Fe$_{78}$Si$_9$B$_{13}$ AMPCs will be presented.

2. Experiments

The commercial ball-milling-crushed Fe$_{78}$Si$_9$B$_{13}$ amorphous powders (China Amorphous Technology CO., LTD, Foshan, China) were sieved into three groups with different particle size ranges, and respectively named as P$_1$, P$_2$ and P$_3$ powders for particle size distributions of 140–170 mesh (90–110 μm), 170–270 mesh (53–90 μm) and 270–400 mesh (38–53 μm). The sodium silicate and the talcum powder were employed as the coating and lubricating agents, respectively.

During a typical fabrication procedure of the AMPCs, the Fe$_{78}$Si$_9$B$_{13}$ powders, consisting of 20 wt.% P$_1$, 60 wt.% P$_2$, and 20 wt.% P$_3$, were first uniformly mixed with 2 wt.% of sodium silicate and 0.6 wt.% of talcum powder. The sodium silicate was sufficiently dissolved with the help of ethyl alcohol (4 wt.%) as the co-solvents. And then, the mixture was molded into green compacts with the dimensions of 26.9 mm in outer diameter, 14.8 mm in inner diameter and 11.2 mm in thickness (Φ26.9 mm × Φ14.8 mm × 11.2 mm) by cold pressing under a pressure of 2.05 GPa. Finally, the compacted cores were orderly dried at 393 K for 120 min, impregnated in dilute sodium silicate under vacuum condition, and annealed at 730 K for 30 min. In this work, three groups of powder core samples were prepared under various particle size distributions, compaction pressures, and coating agent contents. The particle size distribution of the Fe$_{78}$Si$_9$B$_{13}$ powders was tested by a laser particle size analyzer (LPSA, BT-9300ST,

Bettersize Instruments Ltd., Dandong, China). The microstructures and phase structures of the MPCs were examined by a scanning electron microscope (SEM, Phenom ProX, Phenom-World BV, Eindhoven, The Netherlands) and X-ray diffraction (XRD, Rigaku MiniFlex600X, Rigaku Corporation, Tokyo, Japan) with Cu K_α radiation, respectively. The MPCs' effective permeability, μ_e, the frequency characteristic (μ_e-f) when the frequency was the range of 20–100 kHz, within a constant voltage of 0.3 V, and the DC-bias performance were measured by an LCR meter (Wayne Kerr 3260B, Wayne Kerr Electronics, West Sussex, UK). The core losses were measured by a core loss measuring instrument (MATS-2010M, Linkjoin, Loudi, China) at 50 kHz and 100 kHz with a maximum magnetic flux density of 0.1 T, respectively. Among these, the cores were winded in turns of 30 with copper wires of Φ0.6 mm.

3. Results and Discussions

3.1. Microstructure of Amorphous Powders

Figure 1 displays the representative XRD pattern of the ball-milling-crushed $Fe_{78}Si_9B_{13}$ amorphous powders. A broad diffuse peak at around $2\theta = 45°$, without any distinct diffraction peaks, could only be seen for the powders, which validated the formation of an amorphous structure. The inset of Figure 1 shows the morphology of the ball-milling-crushed $Fe_{78}Si_9B_{13}$ amorphous powders with the particle size ranging up to 125 μm. The powders were in the shape of a polygon with smooth edges, which was beneficial to the uniform insulation coating, thereby reducing the eddy current loss between the powders.

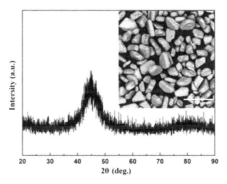

Figure 1. X-ray diffraction (XRD) patterns of the ball-milling-crushed $Fe_{78}Si_9B_{13}$ amorphous powders, the inset shows the scanning electron microscope (SEM) micrograph of the powders

3.2. Particle Size Distribution

Table 1 lists the characterization of particle size distribution, green compact density, ρ, effective permeability, μ_e, and core loss, P_c, for the AMPCs with different matching ratios (mass percent) of P1/P2/P3%. In this table, D10, D25, D50, D75, and D90 represent the specific particle size at which the cumulative frequency showed 10%, 25%, 50%, 75%, and 90%, respectively. The green compact density of the AMPCs was analyzed by the principle of Archimedes. Figure 2 displays the morphology of the AMPCs with different matching ratios. Figure 3 displays the matching ratio dependence of the frequency characteristic and DC-bias performance. We observed the following points. (1) The attenuation rate of μ_e, R_μ, in the frequency band of 20–100 kHz for the AMPCs was 0.92–0.98%. It was indicated that the AMPCs with different matching ratios, given in Table 1, exhibited good constant magnetic properties with the frequency. (2) The circumferential crack was observed at the outer surface of the AMPCs when the mass ratio of the P1 powders was greater than 30 wt.%. This could be due to the increasing number of large pores induced by the increase of the coarse particles (P1 powders with the particle size distribution of 140–170 mesh), which was detrimental to the formability enhancement of the AMPCs [28]. (3) The AMPCs' green compact density, ρ, the effective permeability, μ_e, and the residual effective permeability at the applied magnetizing field of 7.96 kA/m, μ_e@7.96 kA/m, increased first and then decreased with the increasing size of D50, and exhibited a maximum ρ of 5.66 g/cm^3 and a maximum μ_e of 65.54, as the mass ratios of the P1%/P2%/P3% powders were 20:70:10 and 30:60:10, respectively. The AMPCs' μ_e can be calculated using the following equation:

$$\mu_e = \frac{L_s l_e}{\mu_0 N^2 A_e},$$ (1)

where L_s, A_e and l_e are the inductance, the cross-section area, and the mean flux density path length of the ring sample cores, respectively. N is the total number of coil turns and μ_0 is the free space permeability.

It was seen that the magnitude of the μ_e strongly depended on the number and size of pores in the AMPCs according to the l_e in Equation (1). For the AMPCs of numbers 3, 2, and 1, as the mass ratio of fine powders (P3) increased from 10 wt.% to 30 wt.%, the interface between the magnetic particles and the specific surface area of the powders subsequently increased, followed by an increasing number of the pores. Thus, the μ_e and ρ gradually decrease from 64.54 to 53.10, and from 5.66 g/cm^3 to 5.55 g/cm^3. For the AMPCs of numbers 3, 4, and 5, the ratio of the coarse powders (P1) increased from 20 wt.% to 40 wt.%, which would lead to the increasing number of large pores in the AMPCs [28]. Accordingly, the ρ gradually decreased from 5.66 g/cm^3 to 5.52 g/cm^3. The μ_e, however, increased first and then decreased. A small increment of 1.08 for μ_e was observed as the mass ratio of P1%/P2%/P3% changed from 20:70:10 to 30:60:10, which could be attributed to the increase of the average particle size for AMPCs [29].

(4) It is known that the eddy current loss is dominant for the core loss in the high-frequency range. The eddy current loss is inversely proportional to the electrical resistivity but proportional to the square of particle size [30]. It was seen that the P_c gradually increased from 315.2 mW/cm^3 to 409.7 mW/cm^3, at 50 kHz for B_m = 0.1 T, as the size of D50 increased from 66.5 μm to 90.2 μm. Moreover, it was also shown that a small increment of 24.31 mW/cm^3 for the P_c was observed as the ratio of the P3 powders decreased from 30 wt.% to 10 wt.%, with a constant ratio of 20 wt.% for the P1 powder. Based on the discussion above, the matching ratio of 20:70:10 for P1%/P2%/P3% was adopted as a reasonable process parameter for the subsequent fabrication of the AMPCs, because of its higher μ_e, relatively lower P_c, and being easier to shape, compared with the other matching ratios.

Table 1. Characterization of particle size distribution, green compact density, effective permeability, and core loss for the amorphous magnetic powder cores (AMPCs) with different matching ratios of P1%/P2%/P3%.

Matching Ratio (P1%:P2%:P3%)	Characterization of Particle Size Distribution					ρ, g/cm^3	μ_e	P_c@50 kHz, 0.1 T, mW/cm^3
	D10, μm	D25, μm	D50, μm	D75, μm	D90, μm			
No. 1—20:50:30	44.30	50.50	66.50	85.60	114.40	5.55	53.10	315.23
No. 2—20:60:20	46.80	57.40	69.90	89.40	119.80	5.61	58.13	330.85
No. 3—20:70:10	49.50	66.70	74.10	96.30	132.30	5.66	64.46	339.54
No. 4—30:60:10	51.70	70.20	81.10	110.00	141.20	5.63	65.54	374.28
No. 5—40:50:10	53.10	75.30	90.20	123.40	156.40	5.52	61.10	409.76

Figure 2. Morphology of the amorphous magnetic powder cores (AMPCs) with different matching ratios of P1%/P2%/P3%.

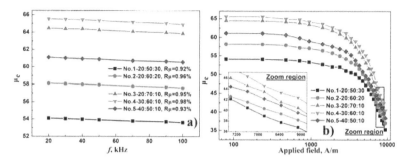

Figure 3. Dependence of matching ratio on frequency characteristic (**a**) and direct current (DC) bias performance (**b**).

3.3. Molding Pressure

Figure 4 shows the SEM micrographs of AMPCs' cross-sections under three different molding pressures of 1.95 GPa, 2.15 GPa, and 2.35 GPa, wherein the matching ratio of P1%/P2%/P3% for the AMPCs was 20:70:10. Figure 5 displays the dependence of the molding pressure on the compact density, the effective permeability, the frequency characteristic, the DC-bias performance, and the core loss for the AMPCs. It was observed that the microstructure of the AMPCs' cross-section consisted of coated powders and pores. The pores showed a three-dimensional network. With the increase of the molding pressure, the pore volume and its ratio gradually reduced. Accordingly, the AMPCs' green compact density, ρ, the effective permeability, μ_e, and the residual effective permeability at an applied field of 7.96 kA/m, μ_e@7.96 kA/m, increased from 5.63 g/cm^3 to 5.86 g/cm^3, from 62.37 to 73.91, and from 42.95 to 46.53, as the molding pressure increased from 1.95 GPa to 2.55 GPa, respectively. The MPCs' P_c decreased first and then increased with the increasing molding pressure, and exhibited a minimum value of 301.92 mW/cm^3 (at 50 kHz for $B_m = 0.1$ T) at a molding pressure of 2.45 GPa. The attenuation ratio of μ_e in the frequency band of 20–100 kHz, R_μ, slowly went down from 1.02% to 0.85% with the increasing molding pressure. This was beneficial to the frequency characteristic improvement of the AMPCs.

Moreover, it was seen from Figure 5a,d that both the μ_e and P_c rapidly increased as the molding pressure surpassed 2.45 GPa. This could be contributed to the damage of the coated insulation material and the increasing residual stress caused by greater molding pressure. When the molding pressure was lower than 2.45 GPa, the increasing process of μ_e could be divided into two different stages: The initial fast increasing stage (1.95–2.25 GPa), and the subsequent stably increasing stage (2.25–2.45 GPa). It was also seen from Figure 5d that a small increment of 4.70 mW/cm^3 for the core loss was observed as the molding pressure decreased from 2.45 GPa to 2.35 GPa. Thus, it was concluded that the molding pressure range of 2.35–2.45 GPa was reasonable for the AMPCs' fabrication.

Figure 4. SEM micrographs of AMPCs' cross-sections under different molding pressures, (**a**) 1.95 GPa, (**b**) 2.15 GPa, and (**c**) 2.35 GPa.

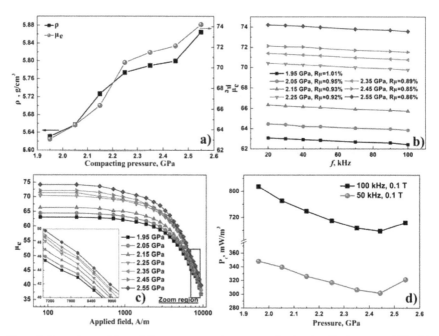

Figure 5. Dependence of the molding pressure on the compact density, the effective permeability (**a**), the frequency characteristic (**b**), the DC-bias performance (**c**), and the core loss (**d**) for the AMPCs.

3.4. Insulating Material Content

Figure 6 shows the SEM micrographs of the coated magnetic powders with three different coating agent (sodium silicate) contents of 0.5 wt.%, 1.0 wt.% and 2.0 wt.%. Figure 7 displays the dependence of the sodium silicate content on the compact density, the effective permeability, the frequency characteristic, the DC-bias performance, and the core loss for the AMPCs with a P1%/P2%/P3% ratio of 20:70:10 and a molding pressure of 2.45 GPa. It was seen that the increase of the coating agent content was beneficial to obtaining an even electro-insulating layer on the surface of the magnetic powders. The attenuation ratio of μ_e, R_μ, in the frequency band of 20–100 kHz was in the range of 0.83%–0.91%. That meant that the AMPCs with different sodium silicate contents all exhibited good frequency stabilities of effective permeability. The AMPCs' core loss, P_c, as shown in the Figure 7d, gradually decreased from 590.54 mW/cm^3 to 248.93 mW/cm^3, at 50 kHz for B_m = 0.1 T, with an increasing content of sodium silicate from 0.5 wt.% to 3.5 wt.%, due to the improving insulation effect for the AMPCs.

As seen from Figure 7a–c, the AMPCs' ρ, μ_e, and μ_e@7.96 kA/m initially increased, but was followed by a decline with the increasing content of sodium silicate. Within the content range of 0.5 wt.%–1.5 wt.%, the ρ increased with the increase of the sodium silicate content. This was due to the lubrication film on the particle surface, generated by the coating agent, which can enhance the mobility of the particles during the compacting process [27,29]. For the μ_e, too low content of sodium silicate (0.5 wt.%, seen in Figure 6a) would result in the increased number of pores, due to the poor bonding effect for the particles in the AMPCs. Thus, a μ_e of 70.49 was observed. As the sodium silicate content increased to 1.0 wt.%, the uneven coating layer on the powder surface—as shown in the Figure 6b—would cause the poor insulation for particles in the AMPCs, and in turn, the μ_e climbed to 81.87. With the improved insulation effect for particles, the μ_e decreased to 77.01 as the sodium silicate content increased to 1.5 wt.%. Moreover, it was also seen that both the ρ and μ_e gradually decreased when the sodium silicate content was greater than 1.5 wt.%, due to the increasing ratio of non-magnetic material (coating agent) in the AMPCs. Therefore, the sodium silicate additive amount of 1.5 wt.% was proposed for the AMPCs' fabrication with a P1%/P2%/P3% mass ratio of 20:70:10 and a molding pressure of 2.45 GPa. And then, an excellent comprehensive soft magnetic property could be obtained as follows: $\mu_e = 77.01$, $0.85\% < R_\mu$, μ_e (at a bias field of 7.96 kA/m) = 49.57, P_c (at 50 kHz for $B_m = 0.1$ T) = 305.23 mW/cm^3, and P_c (at 100 kHz for $B_m = 0.1$ T) = 650.46 mW/cm^3.

Figure 6. SEM micrographs of the coated magnetic powders with three different sodium silicate contents of 0.5 wt.% (a), 1.0 wt.% (b) and 2.0 wt.% (c).

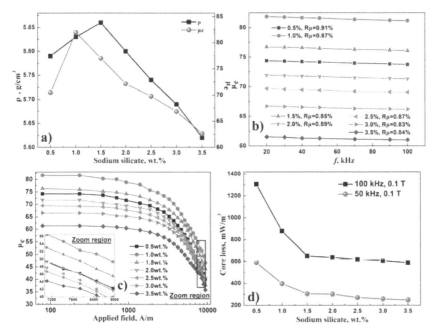

Figure 7. Dependence of the sodium silicate content on the compact density, the effective permeability (**a**), the frequency characteristic (**b**), the DC-bias performance (**c**), and the core loss (**d**) for the AMPCs.

4. Conclusions

The comprehensive soft magnetic properties of the Fe$_{78}$Si$_9$B$_{13}$ AMPCs have been enhanced by the coordinated adjustments of the particle size distribution, the compacting pressure, and the coating agent content in the industrial condition. The optimal magnetic properties of the Fe$_{78}$Si$_9$B$_{13}$ AMPCs can be obtained when the technological parameters are as follows: The matching ratio of P1%/P2%/P3% is 20:70:10 in mass percent, the molding pressure is in the range of 2.35–2.45 GPa, and the additive amount of sodium silicate is 1.5 wt.%. As compared to the original scheme (the P1%/P2%/P3% mass ratio in 20:60:20, the molding pressure in 2.05 GPa, and the sodium silicate content in 2.0 wt.%), the AMPCs' compact density, ρ, the effective permeability, μ_e, and the residual effective permeability at 7.96 kA/m, μ_e@7.96 kA/m, increased from 5.61 g/cm^3 to 5.86 g/cm^3, from 58.13 to 77.01, and from 40.36 to 49.57, respectively, while the core loss reduced from 380.85 mW/cm^3 to 335.23 mW/cm^3 (at 50 kHz for B_m = 0.1 T).

Author Contributions: H.S. and W.C. conceived and designed the experiments; C.W. and J.L. performed the experiments and analyzed the data; H.S. wrote the paper.

Funding: This research was funded by the National Natural Science Foundation of China (Grant No. 51704078), the Province Natural Science Fund of Guangdong (Grant No. 2017A030313312), the university key platform funding projects of Guangdong education department (Grant No. gg041002), the engineering technology research center project of Foshan City (Grant No. 20172010018) and the talent research start-up program of Foshan University (Grant No. gg040942).

Conflicts of Interest: The authors declare no conflict of interest.

References

1. Shokrollahi, H.; Janghorban, K. Soft magnetic composite materials (SMCs). *J. Mater. Process. Technol.* **2007**, *189*, 1–12. [CrossRef]

2. Valchev, V.C.; Todorova, T.P.; Bossche, V.A. Comparison and design of DC chokes based on different magnetic materials. In Proceedings of the 2017 XXVI International Scientific Conference Electronics (ET), Sozopol, Bulgaria, 13–15 September 2017; IEEE: Piscataway, NJ, USA, 2017.

3. Leary, A.M.; Ohodnicki, P.R.; Mchenry, M.E. Soft Magnetic Materials in High-Frequency, High-Power Conversion Applications. *JOM* **2012**, *64*, 772–781. [CrossRef]

4. Sugimura, K.; Shibamoto, D.; Yabu, N.; Yamamoto, T.; Sonehara, M.; Sato, T.; Mizuno, T.; Mizusaki, H. Surface-Oxidized Amorphous Alloy Powder/Epoxy-Resin Composite Bulk Magnetic Core and Its Application to Megahertz Switching LLC Resonant Converter. *IEEE. T. Mag.* **2017**, *53*, 1–6. [CrossRef]

5. Zhang, L.; Li, D.; Lu, Z.; Liu, T.; Guo, F.; Liu, K.; Wang, J.; Zhou, S. Novel Fe-based amorphous magnetic powder cores with ultra-low core losses. *Sci. China. Technol. Sci.* **2010**, *53*, 1290–1293. [CrossRef]

6. Salmi, W.A.; Gyawali, P.; Dahal, B.; Pegg, I.L.; Philip, J. Core-shell FeNi-NixFe3-xO4 nanowires. *J. Vac. Sci. Technol. B* **2015**, *33*, 040604. [CrossRef]

7. Otsuka, I.; Kadomura, T.; Ishiyama, K.; Yagi, K. Magnetic Properties of Fe-Based Amorphous Powder Cores with High Magnetic Flux Density. *IEEE T. Mag.* **2009**, *45*, 4294–4297. [CrossRef]

8. Huang, C.; Liu, T.; Wang, X.; Lu, C.; Li, D.; Lu, Z. Magnetic properties of Fe82Si2B14C2 amorphous powder cores with low core loss and high magnetic flux density. *Powder Metall.* **2014**, *57*, 41–44. [CrossRef]

9. Wei, D.; Wang, X.; Nie, Y.; Feng, Z.; Chen, Y.; Harris, V.G. Low loss Sendust powder cores comprised of particles coated by sodium salt insulating layer. *J. Appl. Phys.* **2015**, *117*, 17A921. [CrossRef]

10. Liu, M.; Huang, K.; Liu, L.; Li, T.; Cai, P.; Dong, Y.; Wang, X. Fabrication and magnetic properties of novel Fe-based amorphous powder and corresponding powder cores. *J. Mater. Sci-Mater. El.* **2018**, *29*, 6092–6097. [CrossRef]

11. Guo, J.; Dong, Y.; Man, Q.; Li, Q.; Chang, C.; Wang, X.; Li, R. Fabrication of FeSiBPNb amorphous powder cores with high DC-bias and excellent soft magnetic properties. *J. Magn. Magn. Mater.* **2016**, *401*, 432–435. [CrossRef]

12. Li, X.; Dong, Y.; Liu, M.; Chang, C.; Wang, X. New Fe-based amorphous soft magnetic composites with significant enhancement of magnetic properties by compositing with nano-(NiZn)Fe2O4. *J. Alloys Compd.* **2017**, *696*, 1323–1328. [CrossRef]

13. Zhao, G.; Wu, C.; Yan, M. Fabrication and growth mechanism of iron oxide insulation matrix for Fe soft magnetic composites with high permeability and low core loss. *J. Alloys Compd.* **2017**, *710*, 138–143. [CrossRef]

14. Xiao, L.; Sun, Y.; Ding, C.; Yang, L.; Yu, L. Annealing effects on magnetic properties and strength of organic-silicon epoxy resin-coated soft magnetic composites. *J. Mech. Eng. Sci.* **2014**, *228*, 2049–2058. [CrossRef]

15. Kollar, P.; Bircakova, Z.; Fuezer, J.; Bures, R.; Faberova, M. Power loss separation in Fe-based composite materials. *J. Magn. Magn. Mater.* **2013**, *327*, 146–150. [CrossRef]

16. Peng, Y.; Yi, Y.; Li, L.; Yi, J.; Nie, J.; Bao, C. Iron-based soft magnetic composites with Al_2O_3 insulation coating produced using sol–gel method. *Mater. Des.* **2016**, *109*, 390–395. [CrossRef]

17. Wang, J.; Fan, X.; Wu, Z.; Li, G. Intergranular insulated Fe/SiO_2 soft magnetic composite for decreased core loss. *Adv. Powder. Technol.* **2016**, *27*, 1189–1194. [CrossRef]

18. Xie, D.; Lin, K.; Lin, S. Effects of processed parameters on the magnetic performance of a powder magnetic core. *J. Magn. Magn. Mater.* **2014**, *353*, 34–40. [CrossRef]

19. Streckova, M.; Hadraba, H.; Bures, R.; Faberova, M.; Roupcova, P.; Kubena, I.; Medvecky, L.; Girman, V.; Kollar, P.; Fuzer, J.; et al. Chemical synthesis of nickel ferrite spinel designed as an insulating bilayer coating on ferromagnetic particles. *Surf. Coat. Technol.* **2015**, *270*, 66–76. [CrossRef]

20. Xie, Y.; Yan, P.; Yan, B. Enhanced Soft Magnetic Properties of Iron-Based Powder Cores with Co-Existence of Fe_3O_4–$MnZnFe_2O_4$ Nanoparticles. *Metals* **2018**, *8*, 702. [CrossRef]

21. Li, B.; Zheng, Z.; Yu, H.; Zeng, D. Improved permeability of Fe based amorphous magnetic powder cores by adding Permalloy. *J. Magn. Magn. Mater.* **2017**, *438*, 138–143. [CrossRef]

22. Yagi, M.; Endo, I.; Otsuka, I.; Yamamoto, H.; Okuno, R.; Koshimoto, H.; Shintani, A. Magnetic properties of Fe-based amorphous powder cores produced by a hot-pressing method. *J. Magn. Magn. Mater.* **2000**, *215–216*, 284–287. [CrossRef]

23. Zheng, Y.; Wang, Y.; Xia, G. Amorphous soft magnetic composite-cores with various orientations of the powder-flakes. *J. Magn. Magn. Mater.* **2015**, *396*, 97–101. [CrossRef]

24. Li, Z.; Dong, Y.; Li, F.; Chang, C.; Wang, X.; Li, R. $Fe_{78}Si_9B_{13}$ amorphous powder core with improved magnetic properties. *J. Mater. Sci-Mater. El.* **2017**, *28*, 1180–1185. [CrossRef]

25. Li, Z.; Dong, Y.; Pauly, S.; Chang, C.; Wei, R.; Li, F.; Wang, X. Enhanced soft magnetic properties of Fe-based amorphous powder cores by longitude magnetic field annealing. *J. Alloys Compd.* **2017**, *706*, 1–6. [CrossRef]

26. Dong, Y.; Li, Z.; Liu, M.; Chang, C.; Li, F.; Wang, X. The effects of field annealing on the magnetic properties of FeSiB amorphous powder cores. *Mater. Res. Bull.* **2017**, *96*, 160–163. [CrossRef]

27. Liu, H.; Su, H.; Geng, W.; Sun, Z.; Song, T.; Tong, X.; Zou, Z.; Wu, Y.; Du, Y. Effect of Particle Size Distribution on the Magnetic Properties of Fe-Si-Al Powder Core. *J. Supercond. Nov. Magn.* **2016**, *29*, 463–468. [CrossRef]

28. Bai, R.; Zhu, Z.; Zhao, H.; Mao, S.; Zhong, Q. The percolation effect and optimization of soft magnetic properties of FeSiAl magnetic powder cores. *J. Magn. Magn. Mater.* **2017**, *433*, 285–291. [CrossRef]

29. Taghvaei, A.; Shokrollahi, H.; Ghaffari, M.; Janghorban, K. Influence of particle size and compaction pressure on the magnetic properties of iron-phenolic soft magnetic composites. *J. Phys. Chem. Solids.* **2010**, *71*, 7–11. [CrossRef]

30. Taghvaei, A.; Shokrollahi, H.; Janghorban, K.; Abiri, H. Eddy current and total power loss separation in the iron–phosphate–polyepoxy soft magnetic composites. *Mater. Des.* **2009**, *30*, 3989–3995. [CrossRef]

Article

Fabrication of Functionally Graded Materials Using Aluminum Alloys via Hot Extrusion

Dasom Kim [1], Kwangjae Park [1], Minwoo Chang [2], Sungwook Joo [3], Sanghwui Hong [3], Seungchan Cho [4] and Hansang Kwon [1,5,*]

[1] Department of Materials System Engineering, Pukyong National University, 365, Sinseon-ro, Nam-gu, Busan 48547, Korea; ds09262000@naver.com (D.K.); pkj3678@naver.com (K.P.)
[2] Department of Research and Development, Daeyeong Metal. Co., Ltd., 1209-7 SinSang-ri Jinryang-eup, Kyungsan 38470, Korea; ngm01@ngm.re.kr
[3] Department of Converged Technology Research, Gyeongbuk Hybrid Technology Institute, Goiyean-dong, Yeongcheon, Gyeongbuk 38899, Korea; ngm06@ngm.re.kr (S.J.); ngm05@ngm.re.kr (S.H.)
[4] Department of Composites Research, Korea Institute of Materials Science, Changwon-daero, Seongsan-gu, Changwon-si, Gyeongsangnam-do 51508, Korea; seungchan.cho@gmail.com
[5] Department of Research and Development, Next Generation Material Co., Ltd., 365, Sinseon-ro, Nam-gu, Busan 48547, Korea
* Correspondence: kwon13@pknu.ac.kr; Tel.: +82-51-629-6383

Received: 20 December 2018; Accepted: 7 February 2019; Published: 11 February 2019

Abstract: In this study, we have attempted to manufacture functionally graded materials (FGMs) using aluminum alloys 3003 and 6063 via a hot extrusion process to realize multifunctionality through achieving high strength and low weight. The FGMs were fabricated using Al3003 powder and Al6063 bulk to improve the interfacial properties. Particle size analysis and X-ray fluorescence of the Al3003 powder were used to analyze the composition of general Al3003; microstructure analysis revealed improved hardness with almost no defects, such as cracks at the interface between the two materials. The experimentally determined tensile strength of the composite was observed to be higher than the theoretical value calculated using the rule of mixtures; the strengthening mechanisms considered for the calculations were grain size reduction and precipitation hardening. In particular, we attempted to predict the strengthening effect resulting from the fine grain size of the powder and grain size reduction due to the extrusion process using the Hall–Petch equation. The Kelly–Tyson equation was also used to calculate the theoretical strength in the presence of the strengthening phases. Based on these results, it was confirmed that FGMs can be successfully produced using the hot extrusion process.

Keywords: functionally graded materials (FGMs); aluminum alloy; hot extrusion; Hall–Petch equation; Kelly–Tyson equation

---

1. Introduction

Lightweight materials have been extensively developed for use in transport machineries, especially in aircrafts, automobiles, and marine vehicles. In particular, aluminum is generally used to realize lightweight in materials. Therefore, aluminum has been used in the form of an alloy by adding other elements by many researchers, such as Al-Stainless steel (SUS) composite and Al-carbon nanotubes (CNT) composite [1–3].

Recently, multifunctionality, where diverse functions are realized in the same material, has been increasingly desired. In this context, the concept of functionally graded materials (FGMs) has been suggested as a method to realize multifunctionality. FGMs are materials in which a gradient in property is created by changing the composition continuously.

Miyamoto et al. introduced the concept of FGMs [4]. This concept facilitates the improvement of the quality of the interfaces in a heterogeneous material to prevent cracks, which arise due to the residual stress resulting from the difference in the properties of the different components in the heterogeneous material.

The FGMs mitigate the differences in the properties between the two materials by forming interlayers; however, this is difficult to control because the layers formed at the interface must be thin and uniform. Besides, cracks are sometimes also observed in the FGMs.

To address these problems, researchers have attempted new fabrication methods, such as centrifugal casting, semi-solid forming under magnetic field, and spark plasma sintering (SPS) [5–7], while extrusion processes such as co-extrusion, indirection, and constant extrusion have been used as a fabrication method for over 30 years [8,9]. Fan et al. attempted to join Al1060 and Al6063 by welding following die extrusion [10]. However, there were many cracks at the interface due to the difficulty in controlling the stress. Kwon et al. tried a hot extrusion process to fabricate an Al-CNT composite [11]. The microstructure was observed to be elongated in a direction parallel to the direction of the extrusion, with no cracks and pores. Furthermore, although the composite includes only one volume, the mechanical properties were significantly improved.

This study attempted to fabricate FGMs via a hot extrusion process. The Al3003/Al6063 FGM fabricated in this study has the shape of a rod, the center axis of which consists of Al3003 and serves as a skeleton for the material; this center is surrounded by Al6063. While Al6063 is an aluminum-based alloy that has high strength and hardness to protect the material from external shock, the Al3003 alloy has excellent ductility, which gives flexibility to the material itself, thereby enhancing workability. Thus, the FGM is suitable for use as a wire material for an industrial electric pole and can also be used as a skeleton for steel structures or automobile structural materials.

For dissimilar materials to be well bonded, the surface area of the contact between the two materials must be large. For example, if the surface is rough and the bulk is in contact with a rugged bulk surface, the area of the contact will be larger. Uehara and Sakurai confirmed the relation between the bonding strength and surface roughness of a joined part, which was controlled by changing the feed in a common mechanical milling machine [12]. They observed that the tensile strength was higher when the surface roughness was increased to ~3–6 μm than when the surface roughness was <1 μm.

Figure 1a shows a schematic diagram of the contact surface between two materials in the bulk form. Under these conditions, the contact surface comprises the area indicated by the straight line where the two materials come into contact. On the other hand, if one material is bulk and the other is a powder (Figure 1b), the contact surface area significantly increases because the powder has a much larger surface area than the bulk. Furthermore, Figure 1c shows a schematic diagram of the contact surface between two materials in powder form. It can be observed that the surface area of the contact is much greater, although it is difficult to handle such bonding experimentally. Therefore, we fabricated the FGMs, as shown in Figure 1b; and expected better interface properties compared to the case when two bulk materials are used.

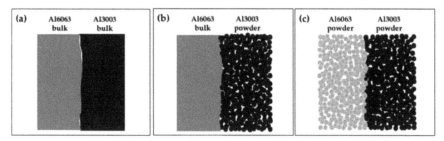

Figure 1. Illustration of the interface between two dissimilar materials. (**a**) bulk–bulk interface, (**b**) bulk–powder interface, and (**c**) powder–powder interface.

To fabricate a sample, we performed canning followed by extrusion. Subsequently, the microstructure of the sample was observed using scanning electron microscopy (SEM), and the composition of the FGMs was analyzed using energy-dispersive spectrometry (EDS). In addition, we used the value of the crystallite size, which was calculated using the Scherrer equation, in the Hall–Petch equation to elucidate the relation between the grain size and strength.

2. Materials and Methods

2.1. Sample Preparation

First, canning was performed as shown in Figure 2. Al3003 powder (965 g; ECKA Granules, purity: 99.5%, particle size: 100 μm) was poured into a bulk Al6063 can (outer diameter: 100 mm and inner diameter: 60 mm) and subjected to a vertical force under a pressure of 5000 kgf. Subsequently, the material was extruded at a temperature of 468 °C, which is below the melting point of both Al3003 and Al6063, using an extrusion machine (SKM Co., Ltd., Incheon, Korea). The temperatures of the billet, container, and mold were 468 °C, 407 °C, and 468 °C, respectively. The ram speed was 2.49 mm/s and the extrusion ratio was 100.

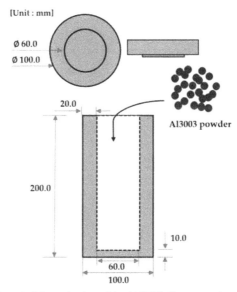

Figure 2. Schematic view of the Al6063 bulk cover and can.

2.2. Analysis of Raw Materials

Particle size analysis (PSA) and X-ray fluorescence (XRF) were used to characterize the Al3003 powder. PSA was first conducted (BECKMAN COULTER, LS 13 320, Indianapolis, IN, USA) followed by XRF to analyze the constituent elements (SHIMADZU, XRF-1800, Tokyo, Japan).

2.3. Characterization of the Samples

First, we used the Archimedes' method to measure the density of the FGMs using a densitometer (KERN, ABJ 120 4M, Balingen, Germany). After etching with 5% NaOH solution, SEM and EDS were employed for a detailed analysis of a sectional area of the samples in detail (TESCAN, VEGA II LSU, city, Czech Republic). Elemental mapping was conducted to determine the ingredient elements of the material (TESCAN, VEGA II LSU, Brno, Czech Republic).

Subsequently, mechanical properties such as hardness and tensile strength were measured using the Vickers hardness test (HM-101, Mitutoyo Corporation, Kanagawa, Japan) according to JIS B 7725 and ISO 6507-2 at five points from the core to the clad (three measurements per point) with a load of 0.3 kg. To measure the tensile stress and strain, a tensile test was conducted on two FGM samples: Al3003/Al6063 FGMs without heat treatment (T-0) and T-5 heat-treated Al3003/Al6063 FGMs (Kyungdo precision Co., Ltd., Siheung, Korea). The no. 4 tensile specimen was fabricated according to KS B 0801 T-5 (width: 6 mm). The treatment is the process that artificially elevates the temperature of the specimen to 150–200 °C, and then cools it [13]. The tensile test was conducted at 24 °C using a 68.65 kN press. Finally, we used the Hall–Petch equation to confirm the relationship between the grain size and tensile strength; the grain size was substituted by the crystallite size, which was calculated using the Scherrer equation and the XRD data (Rigaku, Ultima IV, Tokyo, Japan). Furthermore, the Kelly–Tyson equation was used in this study to calculate the theoretical yield stress of the FGMs.

3. Results

In general, the dispersion of particle size is an important characteristic of a particulate sample and has significant influence on the packing density and porosity of the products.

Figure 3 shows the PSA graph of Al3003 powder with various particle sizes ranging from 10 μm to 280 μm; the average particle size is 125 μm. The accumulate volume graph also shows that the d_{10}, d_{50}, and d_{90} data for the particle size distribution is 35 μm, 97 μm, and 156 μm, respectively.

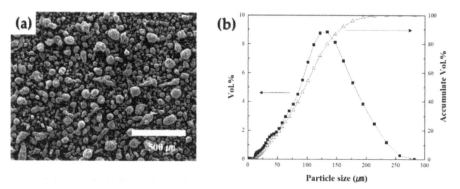

Figure 3. (a) scanning electron microscope (SEM) image of Al3003 powder and **(b)** Typical Particle size analysis (PSA) graph (black squares) and accumulate PSA graph (outlined triangles) of the Al3003 powder used in this study.

When Al3003 powder is filled into the Al6063 bulk can, a high packing density (about 63%) can be achieved as the Al3003 powder has a significantly high degree of dispersion in particle size, which indicates that the density of the FGMs is high.

Table 1 lists the general chemical composition of Al3003 and Al6063. By comparison, Si (1.10%), Mn (0.96%), Fe (0.87%), Zn (0.23%), Cu (0.17%), and Al (96.66%), which is determined by XRF, are present in the Al3003 powder used in this study.

Table 1. General chemical composition of the components Al6063 and Al3003 [14,15].

Material	Chemical Composition (%)									
	Si	Fe	Cu	Mn	Zn	Mg	Cr	Ti	Others	Al
Al6063	0.20–0.60	0.35	0.10	0.10	0.10	0.45–0.90	0.10	0.10	-	97.65–98.50
Al3003	0.6	0.7	0.05–0.20	1.0–1.5	0.10	-	-	-	-	96.90–97.55

We observe that the proportions of the components are approximately in the range of the typical chemical composition of the Al3003 powder (presented in Table 1). Consequently, Al3003 powder, with a mean particle size of 125 μm, was filled into a bulk can made of Al6063, and the final FGM was fabricated via hot extrusion.

Figure 4 shows the photograph of the final material, which is in the shape of a cylindrical rod. Figure 4b shows the cross-section of the FGM, where the inner darker area is composed of Al3003 and the outer brighter area is composed of Al6063. The inner diameter is around 1 mm, and the outer diameter is 8 mm. The density of the FGMs was also measured to confirm that there were nearly no flaws in the material manufactured via hot extrusion. The experimental density measured using the Archimedes' method was 2.6538 g/cm^3 and the theoretical density calculated using the rule of mixtures was 2.7009 g/cm^3. A significantly high relative density of 98.26% was obtained, which confirms the successful fabrication of a dense FGM. Furthermore, it was confirmed that the density of the Al3003 core was nearly 100%. This indicates that hot extrusion is a useful method to form an interface between powders and bulk materials, demonstrating that this process can be used for the fabrication of complex heterogeneous materials.

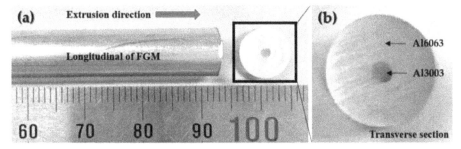

Figure 4. Al3003/Al6063 functionally graded materials (FGMs) fabricated via hot extrusion: (**a**) Photograph of the FGMs and (**b**) high-magnification image of the cross-section of Al3003/Al6063 FGMs.

Figure 5 shows the SEM images of the Al3003/Al6063 FGMs; microstructure analysis was performed to confirm whether the final FGM was fabricated without any cracks and faults. Figures 5d and 5f show the EDS results for Al6063 and Al3003.

By comparing the XRF results, where Mg and Si were determined to be the predominant components of Al6063 and Al3003, respectively, with the EDS result, we infer that Figure 5d corresponds to Al6063 and Figure 5f corresponds to Al3003.

There are no cracks, except for a few pores created via deep etching (Figure 5a) in the region containing Al6063. However, the Al3003 region consists of more pores, which was not observed before conducting the etching process, and moreover, particles were observed, as shown in Figure 5c. This could be because the etching process in Al3003 can be faster and more significant than in Al6063, since the Al3003 is in the form of a powder, which has a higher specific surface area, while Al6063 has higher corrosion resistance compared to Al3003. We also confirmed from the EDS results that the O content is higher in Al3003 than in Al6063. Hence, deep etching was required to observe the microstructure of Al6063, which has high corrosion resistivity. Therefore, these results show that oxidation has occurred more actively in Al3003 than in Al6063. Figure 5b shows the SEM micrograph of the interface between Al6063 and Al3003, demonstrating a distinct and well-formed interface without any flaws, such as cracks. Figure 5e shows a high-magnification micrograph, where no cracks can be observed, except for pores caused by the deep etching similar to Figure 5b.

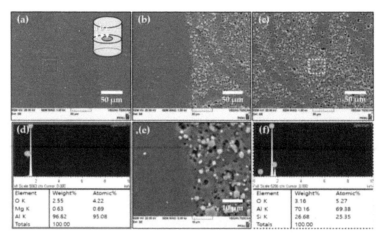

Figure 5. SEM images (**a–c,e**) and EDS results (**d,f**). (**a**) Region constituted by Al6063, (**b**) interface between Al6063 and Al3003, (**c**) region constituted by Al3003, (**d**) EDS of Al6063, (**e**) high-magnification image of the interfacial area between Al6063 and Al3003, and (**f**) EDS of Al3003.

Figure 6 shows the SEM image of a longitudinal section of the Al3003/Al6063 FGM. Figure 6a shows the region containing Al3003, where the pores are larger and longer when the extrusion direction was subjected to pressure and was compressed, whereas the longitudinal section parallel to the direction of extrusion was stretched in the same direction. The interface between Al3003 and Al6063 was analyzed in detail using elemental mapping.

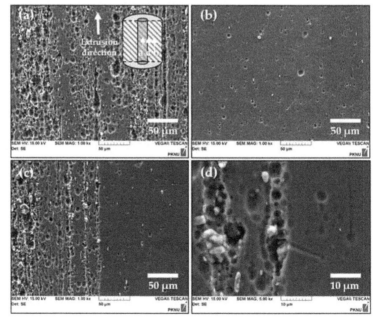

Figure 6. SEM images of the longitudinal section of the FGM. (**a**) Region containing Al3003, (**b**) region containing Al6063, (**c**) interface between Al3003 and Al6063, and (**d**) high-magnification image of the interface between Al3003 and Al6063.

Figure 7b shows the distribution of the relative concentrations of the different components at the interface between Al3003 and Al6063. The particles in the longitudinal section are observed to be relatively larger and have an elongated shape when compared with those observed in the cross-section. Therefore, we can consider that the grains of the FGMs are aligned in the direction of extrusion. Near the interface in the Al3003 area, we expect that the degree of oxidation caused by the deep etching is higher than in the other areas because of the higher O content and lower proportion of Al in this area.

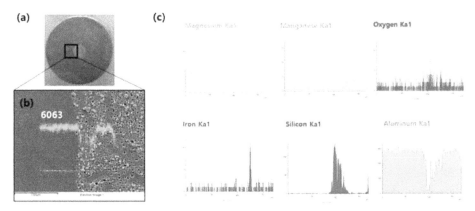

Figure 7. Elemental mapping of the area near the interface between Al6063 and Al3003. (**a**) Picture of a cross-section of the sample, (**b**) SEM image and mapping of all the elements, and (**c**) mapping of the major elements.

In general, while etching is conducted, the grain boundaries are oxidized more than the grain interior. Similarly, the interface is more corrosive due to the disordered arrangement of the atoms. To analyze the mechanical properties, Vickers hardness test and tensile test were conducted.

Figure 8 shows the Vickers hardness values measured on the cross section and longitudinal section of the FGM. The overall hardness in the transverse cross-section is observed to be in the range of 50–53 HV, which is almost 1.5 times greater than that generally observed for both Al3003-T0 and Al6063-T0, as shown in Table 2, and the hardness values are nearly constant. Al6063 has good corrosion resistance, and furthermore, it is fabricated in the bulk form; therefore, it is only slightly oxidized. The high hardness value of 53.03 HV observed at the interface confirms that the Al3003/Al6063 FGM has superior interface properties. Moreover, in the cross-section, although the hardness of the individual parts is slightly different, this difference is not large; therefore, the hardness is uniform.

However, the measured value of the hardness of the longitudinal section is relatively lower when compared to that of the transverse cross-section. This could be because the particle size is further reduced in the cross-section where the grains are subjected to a compressive pressure from all directions, which is less than that in the longitudinal cross-section. While joining two different materials, the properties of the joint play an important role—if the two materials are well bonded, the interfacial properties and the physical properties of the final product are improved.

In contrast, the longitudinal section is elongated in the direction of extrusion and the particles are compressed in a direction vertical to the direction of extrusion.

Table 2. General specifications of mechanical properties of Al6063 and Al3003 [16].

Sample	Density (g/cm³)	Vickers Hardness (HV)	0.2% Offset Yield Strength (MPa)	Tensile Strength (MPa)	Elongation (%)
3003-T0	2.73	30	40	110	28
6063-T0	2.70	26	50	90	-
6063-T5		70	145	185	12

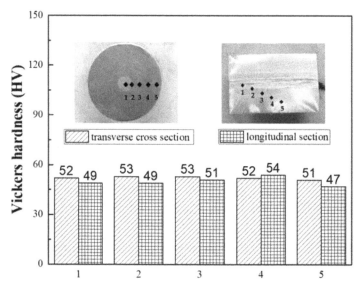

Figure 8. Vickers hardness graph measured on the transverse cross-section and longitudinal sections of the FGM at five regions from the center (Al3003) to Al6063, including the interface between Al3003 and Al6063.

Figure 9 shows the tensile stress–strain graph of the Al3003/Al6063 FGMs (T-0 and T-5). Al3003 and Al6063 have an area ratio of 18:82 at the neck of the tensile specimen. In the case of the T-0 Al3003/Al6063 FGM, the experimental tensile stress is improved to 152.19 MPa, as listed in Table 3, and in the case of the T-5 Al3003/Al6063 FGM, the general tensile stress is improved to 237.29 MPa, which is more than twice the generally observed average tensile stress values for Al3003 and Al6063, as shown in Table 2. The tensile stress of the material satisfies the T6 specification reported by Prillhofer et al. [17]. The elongation of the FGMs without heat treatment is more than 25%, which can solve the formability problem of the general aluminum 6000 series studied by Panigrahi et al. [18].

Furthermore, in the case of T-5 Al3003/Al6063 FGMs, the elongation, which is more than 10%, satisfies the abovementioned T6 specification. To analyze the strengthening mechanism, we considered two possible mechanisms: precipitation hardening and reduction of grain size. In the first mechanism, the precipitates present inside the matrix of the metal play a role in capturing dislocations, which increases the strength and hardness of the material.

Generally, Al alloys have precipitates and in the case of heat-treated alloys, the precipitates are formed and strengthened during the heat treatment. Pokov'a et al. showed that the α-Al$_{12-15}$ (Fe, Mn)$_3$ Si$_{1-2}$ phase and A$_{16}$ (Fe, Mn) phase are generally present in Al3003 [19], and Camero et al. reported that the precipitates in Al6063 such as Mg$_2$Si are generated mainly during heat treatment [20]. These precipitates serve to reinforce the material through a pinning effect. Furthermore, even if the amount and size of the precipitates are the same, the area of the FGMs is reduced by the extrusion process, which indicates that the proportion of the precipitate per unit area increases. Consequently, the movement of the dislocations is significantly inhibited; the strengthening of a material can occur through this mechanism. In the second mechanism, the materials are strengthened due to the reduction in grain size. As the crystal grain size of the material decreases, the grain boundary area increases in general, which disturbs the dislocation migration. Some researchers attempted to calculate the strength of the extruded materials using the Hall–Petch equation. For instance, Uematsu et al. showed that the grain size can be refined by controlling the extrusion conditions (extrusion ratio, working temperature), and showed that the Hall–Petch equation is valid for calculating the strength of the extruded alloys [21].

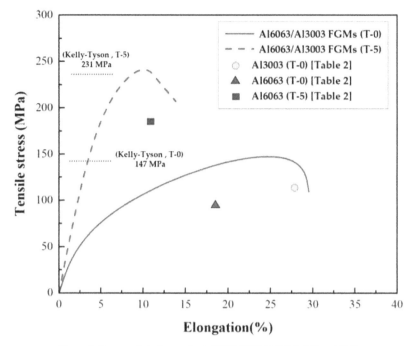

Figure 9. Stress and strain graph of Al3003/Al6063 FGMs (T-0 and T-5).

Furthermore, Kim et al. attempted to control the grain size using equal channel angular pressing, which is an extrusion method, and used the Hall–Petch equation to calculate the yield strength [22]. Thus, it can be concluded that the use of the Hall–Petch equation to calculate the extruded FGMs is valid, and hence, the equation was applied in this study.

To use the Hall–Petch equation, we first calculated the crystallite size by applying the Scherrer equation (Equation (1)). Some researchers applied the crystallite size to the grain size of the Hall-Petch equation, and proved that it is considerably valuable [23]. The Scherrer equation is expressed as follows [24]:

$$\tau = K\lambda/\beta\cos\theta \tag{1}$$

where τ is the mean size of the ordered (crystalline) domains, which may be smaller or equal to the grain size, and K is a dimensionless shape factor with a value close to unity. From the XRD data, the crystallite size of the Al3003 powder is determined to be 48.85 nm, while that of the Al3003/Al6063 FGM is determined to be 44.87 nm. It is thus confirmed that the grain size is decreased owing to the extrusion process and the result shows a possibility of strengthening due to the reduction in the grain size. The values of the crystallite sizes were substituted into the Hall–Petch equation to calculate the yield stress of Al3003 powder and Al3003/Al6063 FGM, as shown in Equation (2). The Hall–Petch equation is expressed as follows [21]:

$$\sigma = \sigma_0 + K_y d^{-1/2} \tag{2}$$

In this equation, σ_0 is the materials constant for the stress in the dislocation movement, K_y is the Hall–Petch slope, which is a strengthening coefficient, and d is the average grain size. It can be observed from this equation that the yield strength in the y-direction increases as the average particle size, d, decreases. In the case of the T-0 Al3003 sample, this effect caused by the reduction in particle size is expected to be observed through improving the material properties via solid-solution strengthening, dispersion strengthening, and work hardening. The value of σ_0 is approximately 58 MPa, while that of s approximately K_y i96 MPa·μm$^{1/2}$, and the yield strength was calculated by substituting the crystallite size obtained from the Scherrer equation into the Hall–Petch equation.

The calculated value of the yield strength before extrusion is 491.92 MPa and that after extrusion is 511.12 MPa, showing an increase of approximately 20 MPa after the extrusion process. The strength of the final material is increased by ~50 MPa in the sample that was not subjected to the heat treatment. Additionally, precipitation hardening also plays a role in increasing the strength. Therefore, it is considered that a combined effect of these factors increases the final strength by 50 MPa.

Notably, the calculated value is much higher than the experimentally measured value. The considerable difference between the two values is possibly because of using the crystallite size instead of the actual grain size for the calculations. For instance, in the case of a polycrystalline material, the crystallite size is generally smaller than the grain size. If the strength were calculated using the actual grain size, which is expected to be larger than the crystallite size, in the Hall–Petch equation, the result is likely to be similar to the experimental value.

However, notably, the crystallite size was reduced after the extrusion process, and the difference between the strength of the raw materials and extruded materials is similar to the difference between the theoretical values calculated using the Hall–Petch equation. Therefore, the Hall–Petch equation is considered to be effective for explaining the tendency of the reduction in the grain size via the extrusion process and the relatively increased value of the strength. However, a more specific analysis is required to demonstrate the exact strengthening mechanisms, as there are possibly other strengthening factors besides the two factors mentioned in this paper.

To analyze the interactions between the increase in strength owing to the strengthening factors and the decrease in strength owing to the limitations (e.g., difficulty in atomic-level bonding of two other materials), further investigations in addition to quantitative and qualitative analytical data including simulations are required.

$$\sigma_y = \sigma_f V_f \left(1 - \frac{l_c}{2l}\right) + \sigma_m \left(1 - V_f\right) \tag{3}$$

Moreover, Kelly and Tyson established the equation for the yield strength of FGMs, in which the matrix and fiber are evenly mixed and aligned in a particular direction with perfect interfacial bonding [25].

Table 3. Experimental mechanical properties of Al6063/Al3003 FGM (T-0, T-5).

Sample		Bulk Density (g/cm3)	Relative Density (%)	Vickers Hardness (HV)	Diameter (mm)	0.2% Offset Yield Strength (MPa)	Tensile Strength (MPa)	Elongation (%)
Al6063/Al3003 functionally graded materials	T0	2.65 ± 0.00	98.26 ± 0.04	52.13 ± 1.03	8.0 ± 0.1	146.11 ± 0.01	152.19 ± 0.1	29.53 ± 1.99
	T5	2.65 ± 0.00	98.26 ± 0.04	75.00 ± 1.05	8.0 ± 0.1	236.79 ± 7.07	237.29 ± 6.57	13.87 ± 2.55

The Kelly–Tyson equation shows that the overall strength is improved by a load transfer to a fiber when a load is applied to a composite material produced by mixing a matrix and fiber, which indicates that the fiber serves as an enhancer. This equation is used for complex composites. When the material is produced through an extrusion process, the grains are elongated in a direction parallel to the extrusion direction, and the material is compressed in the vertical direction.

A previous study confirmed that this phenomenon actually occurs through the micrographs of the longitudinal cross-section of the Al-CNT composite produced via an extrusion process [26].

As shown in Figure 5a, when the pores distributed in Al3003 are examined, the particles are observed to be arranged in the direction of extrusion and the circular shape of the pores is elongated in the direction of the extrusion. Based on this observation, it was concluded that the Kelly–Tyson equation can be applied for the fabricated material used in this study.

Therefore, the Kelly–Tyson equation was employed, assuming that one material plays the role of the fiber and the other one plays the role of the matrix, although the two are not mixed in our case. Assuming that Al3003 is the matrix and Al6063 is the fiber, in the case of the T-0 FGM, the calculated value of the strength is approximately 147 MPa, which is lower than the experimental value (152.19 MPa, as shown in Table 3). In the case of the heat-treated FGM T-5, the calculated value of the strength is expected to increase to approximately 231 MPa. This theoretical value is also lower than the experimental value for T-5 FGM (237.29 MPa, in Table 3). Thus, for both T-0 and T-5 FMGs, the experimental values are observed to be higher than the calculated values, although the difference is small (less than 5%). However, when the theoretical strength was calculated using the rule of mixtures equation, the values were 90.26 MPa (for T-0 FMG) and 183.32 MPa (for T-5 FMG). Thus, although the Al3003/Al6063 FGM fabricated in this study is not a perfectly mixed composite, it can be confirmed that the Kelly–Tyson equation can be applied to this system. Moreover, the higher experimental value indicates that there are additional factors, such as the reduction in particle size and precipitation hardening, which may play a significant role as described earlier.

The Kelly–Tyson equation considers strengthening effects only by fibers; therefore, this equation may not be the most appropriate equation in the present case. However, when considering all the different factors that affect the strengthening of the composites, this equation can be considered as most suitable.

4. Conclusions

The Al3003/Al6063 FGM was successfully fabricated via hot extrusion to realize multifunctionality including high strength and low weight.

The interface between the two materials is clear, with almost no cracks. It can be considered that the extruded FGM has excellent interface properties based on the high Vickers hardness of the interface. When the powder and bulk are in contact, the surface area of the contact could be larger than that between two bulks, so that the interface was improved.

The tensile strength of the final material subjected to T-5 heat treatment was observed to improve to twice that generally observed for Al3003 and Al6063, and the elongation was greater than 10%. From these results, it can be confirmed that the final product has a high strength and adequate elongation, which are the objectives of this study.

To analyze the strengthening mechanisms, i.e., precipitation hardening and grain refinement, strengthening via grain refinement was emphasized more in this study. Generally, the grain size of the powder is finer than the bulks and the presence of many grain boundaries hinders the grain growth. Therefore, the FGM fabricated using Al3003 powder could be strengthened by the fine grain size. Moreover, the grain size would be reduced by the extrusion process because the grains were subjected to mechanical stress. The Hall–Petch equation was used to explain the tendency for improved strength, which is appropriate for the explanation of the tendency of the increase in strength when the FGM was extruded; this was reported by earlier researchers, as well as observed in our study.

In addition, when the Kelly–Tyson equation was used assuming that Al6063 was a fiber, the theoretical results nearly corresponded to the experimental values. Therefore, the Kelly–Tyson equation could also be used to predict the strength of the extruded FGMs.

In summary, Al-alloy-based FGMs with lightweight and high strength properties were successfully fabricated via hot extrusion. Thus, it could be confirmed that hot extrusion is useful to fabricate FGMs with improved mechanical properties.

Author Contributions: D.K. and K.P. conducted the overall experiments; M.C., S.J., and S.H. fabricated materials via a hot extrusion process and conducted the heat treatment; the tensile test was conducted by S.C.; writing—original draft preparation, D.K.; writing—review and editing, H.K.; visualization, D.K.; supervision, H.K.; project administration, H.K.; and funding acquisition, H.K.

Funding: This research was funded by Ministry of SMEs and Startups (MSS).

Acknowledgments: This research was financially supported by the Ministry of SMEs and Startups (MSS), Korea, under the "Regional Specialized Industry Development Program" supervised by the Korea Institute for Advancement of Technology (KIAT), (2017_R0006154).

Conflicts of Interest: The authors declare no conflict of interest.

References

1. Kelkar, A.; Roth, R.; Clark, J. Automobile bodies: Can aluminum be an economical alternative to steel? *JOM* **2002**, *53*, 28–32. [CrossRef]

2. Park, K.; Park, J.; Kwon, H. Fabrication and characterization of Al-SUS316L composite materials manufactured by the spark plasma sintering process. *Mater. Sci. Eng. A* **2017**, *691*, 8–15. [CrossRef]

3. Morsi, K.; Esawi, A. Effect of mechanical alloying time and carbon nanotubes (CNT) content on the evolution of aluminum (Al)-CNT composite powders. *J. Mater. Sci.* **2007**, *13*, 4954–4959. [CrossRef]

4. Miyamoto, Y.; Kaysser, W.A.; Rabin, B.H.; Kawasaki, A.; Ford, R.G. *Functionally Graded Materials: Design, Processing and Applications, the Characterization of Properties*; Kluwer Academic Publishers: Boston, MA, USA; London, UK, 1999, pp. 89–160.

5. Watanabe, Y.; Inaguma, Y.; Sato, H.; Miura-Fujiwara, E. A novel fabrication method for functionally graded materials under centrifugal force: The centrifugal mixed-powder method. *Materials* **2009**, *2*, 2510–2525. [CrossRef]

6. Liu, T.; Wang, Q.; Gao, A.; Zhang, C.; Wang, C.; He, J. Fabrication of functionally graded materials by a semi-solid forming process under magnetic field gradients. *Scr. Mater.* **2007**, *57*, 992–995. [CrossRef]

7. Kwon, H.; Leparoux, M.; Kawasaki, A. Functionally graded dual-nanoparticulate-reinforced aluminum matrix bulk materials fabricated by spark plasma sintering. *J. Mater. Sci. Technol.* **2014**, *30*, 736–742. [CrossRef]

8. Vouler, T.J.; Clayton, J.D. Heterogeneous deformation and spall of an extruded tungsten alloy: Plate impact experiments and crystal plasticity modeling. *J. Mechanics and Physics of Solids* **2008**, *56*, 297–335. [CrossRef]

9. Cocen, U.; Onel, K. Ductility and strength of extruded SiCp/aluminum-alloy composites. *Comp. Sci. and Technol.* **2002**, *62*, 275–282. [CrossRef]

10. Fan, X.; Chen, L.; Chen, G.; Zhao, G.; Zhang, C. Joining of 1060/6063 aluminum alloys based on porthole die extrusion process. *J. Mater. Process. Technol.* **2017**, *250*, 65–72. [CrossRef]

11. Kwon, H.; Leparoux, M. Hot extruded carbon nanotube reinforced aluminum matrix composite materials. *Nanotechnology* **2012**, *23*, 415701. [CrossRef]

12. Uehara, K.; Sakurai, M. Bonding strength of adhesives and surface roughness of joined parts. *J. Mater. Process. Technol.* **2002**, *127*, 178–181. [CrossRef]

13. William, H.C. *Metals Handbook Vol. 4: Heat Treating*, 9th ed.; American Society for Metals: Metals Park, OH, USA, 1981; p. 216.

14. 3003 (AlMn1Cu, 3.0517, A93003) Aluminum. Available online: https://www.makeitfrom.com/material-properties/3003-AlMn1Cu-3.0517-A93003-Aluminum (accessed on 13 August 2018).

15. Alcoa. Alloy 6063 Datasheet. Available online: https://web.archive.org/web/20031006212043/http://www.alcoa.com/adip/catalog/pdf/Extruded_Alloy_6063.pdf (accessed on 1 November 2006).

16. Kaufman, J.G. Properties of Aluminum Alloys: Fatigue Data and the Effects of Temperature, Product Form, and Processing. ASM International: Metal Park, OH, USA, 2008; pp. 9–17.

17. Prillhofer, R.; Rank, G.; Berneder, J.; Antrekowitsch, H.; Uggowitzer, P.J.; Pogatscher, S. Property criteria for automotive Al-Mg-Si sheet alloys. *Materials* **2014**, *7*, 5047–5068. [CrossRef] [PubMed]

18. Panigrahi, S.K.; Jayaganthan, R.; Pancholi, V. Effect of plastic deformation conditions on microstructural characteristics and mechanical properties of Al 6063 alloy. *Mater. Des.* **2009**, *30*, 1894–1901. [CrossRef]

19. Pokov´a, M.; Cieslar, M.; Lacaze, J. Enhanced AW3003 aluminum alloys for heat exchangers. *WDS* **2011**, *11*, 141–146.

20. Camero, S.; Puchi, E.S.; Gonzalez, G. Effect of 0.1% vanadium addition on precipitation behavior and mechanical properties of Al-6063 commercial alloy. *J. Mater. Sci.* **2006**, *41*, 7361–7373. [CrossRef]

21. Uematsu, Y.; Tokaji, K.; Kamakura, M.; Uchida, K.; Shibata, H.; Bekku, N. Effect of extrusion conditions on grain refinement and fatigue behaviour in magnesium alloys. *Mater. Sci. Eng. A* **2006**, *434*, 131–140. [CrossRef]

22. Kim, W.J.; An, C.W.; Kim, Y.S.; Hong, S.I. Mechanical properties and microstructures of an AZ61Mg Alloy produced by equal channel angular pressing. *Scr. Mater.* **2002**, *47*, 39–44. [CrossRef]

23. Ong, C.Y.A.; Blackwood, D.J.; Li, Y. The effects of W content on solid-solution strengthening and the critical hall-petch grain size in Ni-W alloy. *Surf. Coat. Technol.* **2019**, *357*, 23–27. [CrossRef]

24. Monshi, A.; Foroughi, M.R.; Monshi, M.R. Modified scherrer equation to estimate more accurately nano-crystallite size using XRD. *World J. Nano. Sci. Eng.* **2012**, *2*, 154–160. [CrossRef]
25. Kelly, A.; Tyson, W.R. Tensile properties of fibre-reinforced metals: Copper/tungsten and copper/molybdenum. *J. Mech. Phys. Solids* **1965**, *13*, 329–350. [CrossRef]
26. Kwon, H.; Estili, M.; Takagi, K.; Miyazaki, T.; Kawasaki, A. Combination of hot extrusion and spark plasma sintering for producing carbon nanotube reinforced aluminum matrix composites. *Carbon* **2009**, *47*, 570–577. [CrossRef]

Article

Balancing Porosity and Mechanical Properties of Titanium Samples to Favor Cellular Growth against Bacteria

Ana Civantos [1,*], Ana M. Beltrán [2,*], Cristina Domínguez-Trujillo [2], Maria D. Garvi [3], Julián Lebrato [3], Jose A. Rodríguez-Ortiz [2], Francisco García-Moreno [4], Juan V. Cauich-Rodriguez [5], Julio J. Guzman [2] and Yadir Torres [2]

[1] Micro and Nanotechnology Laboratory, University of Illinois at Urbana-Champaign, Urbana, IL 61801, USA

[2] Departamento de Ingeniería y Ciencia de los Materiales y del Transporte, Escuela Politécnica Superior, Universidad de Sevilla, Virgen de África 7, 41011 Sevilla, Spain; cdominguez10@us.es (C.D.-T.); jarortiz@us.es (J.A.R.-O.); juguzpe@gmail.com (J.J.G.); ytorres@us.es (Y.T.)

[3] Grupo TAR, Escuela Politécnica Superior, Universidad de Sevilla, 41004 Sevilla, Spain; mgarvi@us.es (M.D.G.); grupotar@us.es (J.L.)

[4] Institute of Applied Materials, Helmholtz-Zentrum Berlin für Materialien und Energie, Hahn-Meitner-Platz 1, 14109 Berlin, Germany; garcia-moreno@helmholtz-berlin.de

[5] Unidad de Materiales, Centro de Investigación Científica de Yucatán A. C., 97205 Mérida, Yucatán, Mexico; jvcr@cicy.mx

* Correspondence: ancife@illinois.edu (A.C.); abeltran3@us.es (A.M.B.)

Received: 6 September 2019; Accepted: 22 September 2019; Published: 24 September 2019

Abstract: Two main problems limit the success of titanium implants: bacterial infection, which restricts their osseointegration capacity; and the stiffness mismatch between the implant and the host cortical bone, which promotes bone resorption and risk of fracture. Porosity incorporation may reduce this difference in stiffness but compromise biomechanical behavior. In this work, the relationship between the microstructure (content, size, and shape of pores) and the antibacterial and cellular behavior of samples fabricated by the space-holder technique (50 vol % NH_4HCO_3 and three ranges of particle sizes) is established. Results are discussed in terms of the best biomechanical properties and biofunctional activity balance (cell biocompatibility and antibacterial behavior). All substrates achieved suitable cell biocompatibility of premioblast and osteoblast in adhesion and proliferation processes. It is worth to highlighting that samples fabricated with the 100–200 μm space-holder present better mechanical behavior—in terms of stiffness, microhardness, and yield strength—which make them a very suitable material to replace cortical bone tissues. Those results exposed the relationship between the surface properties and the race of bacteria and mammalian cells for the surface with the aim to promote cellular growth over bacteria.

Keywords: bone implant; porous titanium; cellular adhesion; bacteria colonization; osseointegration

1. Introduction

Longer life expectancy, traumas, and congenital diseases have led to an increase in the use of implants. Bone metal implants are usually made of commercially pure titanium (c.p. Ti) or based on Ti alloys owing to its biocompatibility and mechanical behavior [1]. C p Ti has a Young's Modulus of 100–110 GPa, which is higher than cortical bone (20–25 GPa), causing stress shielding phenomena and bone resorption [2]. This problem can be solved using porous material instead of fully-dense one [3–6]. However, in order to achieve a biomechanical balance (stiffness vs. mechanical strength) of the bone tissue to be replaced, an adequate porosity (in terms of size, shape, and distribution of the pores) is required. Up to 34 processing routes to fabricate porous materials have been already reported [7–10].

Among them, the use of space-holders stands out. This technique uses particles—such as salt [11,12], sugar [13], ammonium bicarbonate [14], or magnesium [15]—to reproduce a bone-like porosity structure in which the space-holder particles can be removed by thermal process or dissolution. This step can be performed before or during the sintering process. The particle size and morphology are key factors in the design of the pore structure. One remarkable advantage is that the space-holder is a cost-effective and non-toxic method, which does not release any toxic agent which could affect cellular and bacterial behavior.

On the other hand, several authors have reported that surface properties such as the topography, roughness, chemistry, and free energy of metallic based biomaterials have a strong influence on the initial adhesion and early differentiation of osteoblast cells [16,17]. In 1987, Cristina was the first author to use the term "the race" for the surface, regarding the competition established between bacteria and cells for the biomaterial surface [18]. Also, Gristina remarked that if bacteria attached and colonize faster than osteoblast cells—i.e., bacteria wins the race—an infection will take place, which will be almost impossible to remove. This effect is due to the fast process of bacteria to excrete extracellular polymeric substances (EPS) once they are attached. The size is one the most highlighted difference: osteoblasts are bigger in size, ranging from 20–30 μm, bacteria such as *Escherichia coli* (*E. coli*) or *Staphylococcus aureus* (the most common bacteria presented in titanium dental implants) are around 1–2 μm in length [19]. The stiffness, surface topography (i.e., roughness) and surface chemistry can be tailored in order to promote an advanced cell adhesion process. It has been described the high stiffness behavior of bacteria compared to osteoblast cells, which can be a potential factor in bacteria adhesion and colonization [20]. However, the adhesion mechanisms and the proliferation rate of bacteria are key factors that favor bacteria in the race for the surface. Filia, pili, and the expression of EPS, which constitute the biofilm formation, are some of the mechanisms that participate in the interactions between bacteria and the surface. This EPS covers and protects the bacteria under a biofilm. In this scenario, bacteria becomes more resistant and the antibiotic treatment usually has no effect. On the other hand, osteoblast cells require a more complex mechanism involving integrin receptors and proteins to develop focal adhesion (FA) points. The FA are based of filopodia and lamellipodia cytoplasmatic projections that control and regulate cell to cell interactions and cell surface as well. Therefore, the control of surface properties may reduce or avoid the bacteria attachment resulting in the successful application of the implant on bone regeneration [19].

In a previous work, we reported the manufacture of porous substrates by the space-holder technique which showed a decrease of bacteria attachment [21]. However, the vast majority of studies which focus on Ti implants made use of either bacteria or celld independently and, thus made it difficult to analyze of what type of surface properties may enhance infections and/or osseointegration. Therefore, here we report for the first time the behavior of bacteria and two murine cell lines (myoblast and osteoblast) on c.p. Ti porous substrates with the aim to design a porous implant able to promote bone regeneration and avoid bacterial infections. In this context, this work examines a detailed study of the influence of microstructural characteristics (size, shape, area, and porosity roughness) on the macro and micro-mechanical behavior, as well as the response of the material in the presence of eukaryotic cell cultures (C2C12-GFP and MC3T3E1) and *E. coli* strain bacteria (Gram-negative bacteria).

2. Materials and Methods

2.1. Fabrication of Ti substrates

The blends of medical grade 4 c.p. Ti were supplied by SE-JONG (Materials Co. Ltd. Gojan-dong Korea). Fully-dense c.p. Ti samples were obtained by conventional powder technology (PM), while porous substrates were fabricated using space-holder technique (50 vol % NH_4HCO_3 and different ranges of particle size: 100–200 μm, 250–355 μm, and 355–500 μm). The green samples were produced by pressing at 800 MPa by means of an Instron 5505 universal testing machine (Instron, High Wycombe, UK). Then, the spacer was thermally removed (firstly at 60 °C and, then at 110 °C under low vacuum conditions), both stages of the thermal treatment are carried out for 10–12 h and low vacuum conditions of 10^{-2} mbar). Subsequently, the samples (porous and fully-dense) were sintered in a ceramic tubular furnace during 2 h at 1250 °C under high vacuum conditions (~10^{-5} mbar).

2.2. Microstructural and Mechanical Characterization

Different techniques were employed to characterize the porosity at different levels (superficial and volumetric), as well as the pore distribution, shape, and roughness previously reported [3–5,14]. Total porosity was determined by both Archimedes' method and image analysis (IA), using a Nikon Epiphot optical microscope (Japan) coupled with a Jenoptik Progres C3 camera and Image-Pro Plus 6.2 analysis software. Confocal laser and scanning electron microscopy (SEM, JEOL JSM-6490LV, JEOL, Tokyo, Japan) were used to evaluate the roughness. Considering the importance of pores roughness on bacterial adhesion, X-ray micro-computed tomography (M-CT) was also performed due to its capability to provide three-dimensional (3D) surface roughness data, among other parameters. These measurements were performed using a custom made X-ray scanner composed mainly of a micron focused X-ray source L8121-01 (with a W-target) from Hamamatsu, Japan [22]. Scans were performed at 100 kV and 100 µA, with a spot size of 5 µm and were recorded with a flat panel detector C7943 (120 × 120 mm, 2240 × 2368 pixel), also from Hamamatsu. A 3D reconstruction of the specimen was obtained by acquiring a certain number of X-ray projections during sample rotation over 360°, followed by software reconstruction of these projections. This method allowed for the qualitative and quantitative exploration of the interior structure of the porous Ti samples, with a pixel size down to 6.4 µm at a 7.8-fold magnification. Parameters such as equivalent diameter (D_{eq}), total porosity (P_t), and interconnected porosity (P_i) was determined by M-CT. All these analytical techniques have been implemented, following the procedures described in previous works [3–5,14].

On the other hand, the macro-mechanical behavior of Ti substrates was evaluated by ultrasound technique (dynamic Young's modulus, E_d) and uniaxial compression test (Young's modulus, E_c; yield strength, σ_y). For mechanical compression testing, the specimen dimensions were fixed to standard recommendation (height/diameter = 0.8). The tests were carried out with a universal electromechanical Instron machine 5505 by applying a strain rate of 0.005 mm/mm/min. All tests finished for a strain of 50 pct. The Young's modulus estimation from the compression stress–strain curves was corrected with the testing machine stiffness (87.9 kN/mm). On the other hand, conventional microhardness studies (Vickers indenter Shimadzu, model HMV-G, Japan) at two different applied loads (HV0.3 and HV1) were performed. All the measures were taken three times per substrate type and applied load.

2.3. In Vitro Cellular Experiments

2.3.1. Analysis of Bacterial Behavior of Porous Substrates

E. coli strain Bacterial behavior on porous and fully-dense c.p. Ti substrates is studied, following the protocol summarized in Figure 1. The used *E. coli* was a lyophilized form from Ielab, Spain (*E. coli*; ATCC 25922). The culture solution was prepared with Peptone Water (dehydrated culture media, from Panread AppliChem, Spain) and *E. coli*-Coliforms Chromogenic Medium from Conda Laboratories S.A. The initial concentration of colony-forming units per 100 mL (CFU/100 mL), was determined by membrane filtration, followed by incubation of the membrane on a Petri plate containing *E. coli*-Coliforms Chromogenic Medium at 37 °C for 24 h. Specifically, the study includes three initial concentrations: $7.8\cdot10^4$ (C1), $3.3\cdot10^3$ (C2), and $4.3\cdot10^2$ (C 3) CFU/100 mL, respectively.

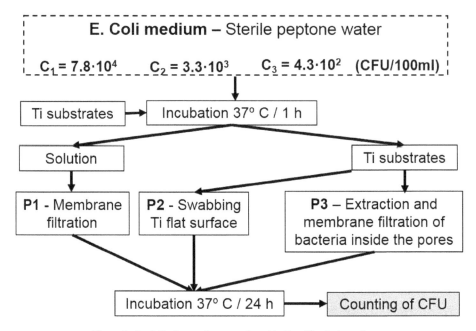

Figure 1. Analytical procedures employed to *E. coli* bacteria analyses.

For *E. coli* bacterial behavior studies, fully-dense and porous substrates were placed in 10 mL test tubes containing each bacterial concentration and these were incubated at 37 °C for 1 h. One tube containing only bacteria was used as reference (R).

Afterwards, the bacterial growth was analyzed by three protocols (Figure 1). Protocol 1 (P1) quantified the amount of *E. coli* per tube and per initial concentration by membrane filtration (pore size of the membrane: 0.45 µm) of the solution of each tube [23]. Protocol 2 (P2) evaluated the *E. coli* density on the Ti substrate using a sterile swab to smear the total surface of the Ti samples. P2 was applied on the flat surface, meaning the areas of the samples without pores. Then, the swab was applied following a zigzag pattern on a Petri dish containing *E. coli*-Coliforms Chromogenic Medium and incubated at 37 °C for 24 h. Protocol 3 (P3) analyzed the *E. coli* proliferation inside the pores by re-immersing the swabbed substrates in test tubes with 10 mL of sterile Peptone water. This solution was mixed using a vortex mixer for 1 min and cooled at 4 °C for 2 h. Tube contents were again mixed with the vortex mixer to detach the bacteria from the cavities and to quantify them using membrane filtration. To guarantee the complete detachment of bacteria from the cavities, the process was repeated three times instead of doing it only once as recommended by ISO 11737:1:2007 standard [24]. The bacterial growth was expressed in total number of CFU for each substrate and concentration. Several measurements were made for each condition (protocol, substrate, and initial concentration).

2.3.2. Evaluation of Cell Adhesion and Proliferation of Eukaryotic Murine C2c12-Gfp Premioblast Cells

Attachment and proliferation of C2C12-GFP were analyzed by inverted fluorescence microscopy (Olympus IX51) and CellD Software (Olympus). To that end, C2C12 murine premioblastic cell line was purchased to America Type Culture Collection (ATCC®CRL-1772™) and transfected, via lentivirus, to self-express constitutively green fluorescent protein (GFP). The presence of this GFP group in cells membrane allowed us to detect the cells and follow the adhesion and proliferation process. The routing passage was performed using DMEM (Dulbecco's modified Eagle medium, Sigma Aldrich), completed with 10% fetal bovine serum (FBS) and 1% of penicillin/streptomycin (100 U/mL, Invitrogen, Germany). For adhesion and proliferation studies, cells were seeded at an initial density of 10,000 cells/cm^2, and after 24 h samples were transferred to new 24-well plates and inverted fluorescent images were taken after day 1, 4, 7, and 10 of cell incubation. The complete medium was changed every 2–3 days. This protocol is summarized in Figure 2.

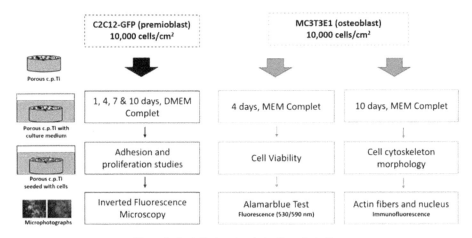

Figure 2. Analytical protocols for the cell studies.

2.3.3. Cell adhesion and Proliferation Studies of Murine MC3T3E1 Osteoblast

A bone cell line, MC3T3-E1 (ATCC CRL-2593), was employed to evaluate the effect of porosity in cell viability, cell proliferation, and cell morphology of osteoblast. The subculture routing was performed in MEM (minimum essential medium, Sigma Aldrich, Germany), completed with 10% fetal bovine serum (FBS) and 1% of penicillin/streptomycin (100U/mL, Invitrogen, Germany). 75 cm^2 culture flasks were placed in a humid atmosphere with 5% CO_2 at 37 °C. Ti substrates were seeded at 10,000 cells/cm^2 and after 24 h samples were transferred to new 24-well plates. Figure 2 summaries the protocol for this study.

Cell Viability of Murine MC3T3E1 Osteoblast

Cell metabolic analysis was measured in order to evaluate the cell viability at day 4 of cell incubation. To that end, AlamarBlue assay (DAL1100, Thermofisher, USA) was performed following the manufacturer's instructions. For this, samples previously seeded with cells were transferred to new 24-well plates and fresh media containing AlamarBlue dye added (10% of culture media volume). After 1.5 h of incubation in darkness at 37 °C, samples were removed and fluorescence signal was read in a microplate reader (Synergy HT, Biotek) using an excitation wavelength of 530 nm and emission wavelength of 590 nm. Fully dense surface was considered control surface as 100% viability. Assays were carried out by triplicate for each sample condition.

Cellular Morphology Evaluation of Murine MC3T3E1 Osteoblast

After 10 days of cell incubation, osteoblast cells attached to the substrates were washed twice with PBS, and subsequently, fixed using 4% paraformaldehyde (PFA) solution. Fully-dense and porous Ti samples were rinsed carefully with PBS twice, permeabilized with 0.1% (v/v) Triton X-100 and, finally, washed again with PBS. The actin cytoskeleton was stained with Texas Red®-X phalloidin (Molecular Probes). To that end, the commercial solution was prepared in PBS and left in dark conditions for 20 min at room temperature (RT). Hoechst (Invitrogen, Molecular Probes) was employed as a contrast marker, to detect cell nuclei. Fully-dense and porous substrates were analyzed using an inverted fluorescence microscope (Olympus IX51) with a TRICT filter (λex/λem = 550/600 nm) for Actin, and DAPI filter for Hoechst (λex/λem = 380/455 nm) and images were treated by CellD analysis software (Olympus).

Statistical Analysis

In general, each experiment was performed in triplicate with each bacteria or cell line, media, and sample. Mean values and standard deviation are reported. A p-value of < 0.01 was deemed to be statistically significant. For in vitro cells, mean and standard deviation are presented and a one-way ANOVA followed by a post Tukey analysis was performed in which values were be statistically significant when p-value was < 0.05.

3. Results

3.1. Microstructural Characterization

Results concerning to the microstructural characterization of the porous substrates can be observed in Figures 3 and 4. Particularly, Figure 3 (top) shows micro-images of the fabricated samples while Figure 3 (bottom) displays details about the aspect of the pores, size, and distribution as obtained by IA. So, by the micro-image we have an overview of the fabricated samples, while by IA details about the aspect of the pores, size and distribution can be determined. Figure 4 shows data obtained by M-CT which provides three-dimensional information, quite useful to determine the distribution of inner pores as well as the roughness volume percentage of the eroded pore compared to the virtually smoothed pore in dependence of the pore equivalent diameter. The presence of micro-scale roughness pattern within the pores was revealed by M-CT, so total inner surface was calculated analyzing a M-CT representative fraction of total sample volume, taking into account the local deviation of the gray values perpendicular to the contour line within a search distance of 20 µm. Data obtained by the analyses of the images contained in Figures 3 and 4 are summarized in Tables 1 and 2, such as porosity and parameters to characterize the pores (equivalent diameter of pores, D_{eq}, shape factor, and roughness).

Table 1. Total, interconnected, and isolated porosity evaluated by different characterization techniques.

Samples		P_T (%)			P_i (%)	
		Archimedes' Method	IA	M-CT	Archimedes' Method	M-CT
Fully-dense		2.3 ± 0.1	1.2 ± 0.2	–	2.1 ± 0.1	–
Spacer size (µm)	100–200	44.8 ± 0.1	50.3 ± 1.3	52.2 ± 10.7	43.1 ± 0.2	51.3 ±10.6
	250–355	45.9 ± 0.2	48.7 ± 1.9	–	41.0 ± 0.1	–
	355–500	46.0 ± 0.1	47.1 ± 4.3	56.4 ± 11.1	41.2 ± 0.2	55.6 ±10.2

Table 2. Morphological features of the pores: size, shape factor, and roughness of the pore walls.

Samples		AI		M-CT	
		D_{eq} (µm)	Shape factor	D_{eq} (µm)	Roughness, R_a (%)
Fully-dense		5.5 ± 0.2	0.99 ± 0.01		–
Spacer size (µm)	100–200	161.1 ± 28.5	0.67 ± 0.03	191.8 ± 6.1	11.3 ± 2.5
	250–355	261.5 ± 9.0	0.67 ± 0.01	311.9 ± 8.2	7.3 ± 2.0
	355–500	293.4 ± 28.2	0.71 ± 0.03	368.4 ± 9.1	3.3 ± 0.6

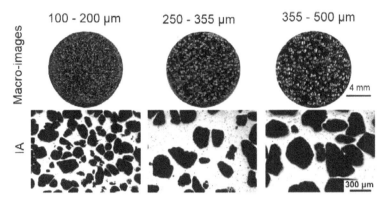

Figure 3. Macro-photography of the samples and optical microscopy images of the porous substrates for the different ranges of spacer particles size: 100–200 μm, 250–355 μm, and 355–500 μm.

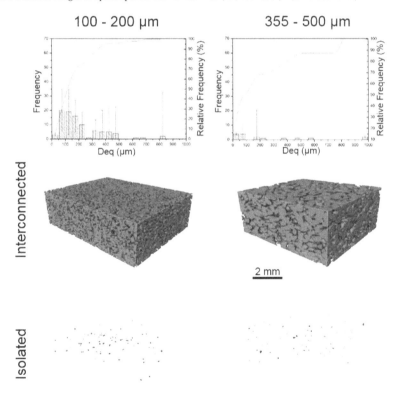

Figure 4. Equivalent diameter determined and interconnected and isolated porosity analyzed by M-CT for two different ranges of spacer particles size: 100–200 μm and 355–500 μm.

3.2. Mechanical Behavior

The macro-mechanical (stiffness, yield strength) and micro-mechanical (Vickers hardness) behavior of porous c.p. Ti is summarized in Table 3. Young's modulus has been measured by ultrasound and uniaxial compression test. These results have been discussed in terms of the advantages and disadvantages of both techniques. On the other hand, the influence of the indentation load and its relationship with the size of the remaining Ti matrix among pores is evaluated. In this context, it should be noted that, for a fixed percentage of total porosity, an increase in pore size implies an increase in the mean distance between pores (the size of the titanium matrix increases).

Table 3. Macro and micro-mechanical behavior of porous substrates.

Samples		US	Uniaxial Compression Test			Microhardness	
		E_d (GPa)	E_c (GPa)	σ_y (MPa)		HV0.3	HV1
Fully-dense		101.2 ± 0.3	95 ± 1.0	628 ± 5		377 ± 26	342 ± 52
Spacer size (μm)	100 200	20.8 ± 0.1	26.0 ± 0.9	127 ± 21		401 ± 42	167 + 81
	250–355	22.8 ± 0.2	23.1 ± 1.0	118 ± 14		356 ± 35	152 ± 72
	355–500	20.0 ± 0.7	19.7 ± 1.2	98 ± 18		350 ± 36	138 ± 70

3.3. Bacteria Behavior

The number of CFU of *E. coli* on titanium substrates as a function of initial bacteria concentration following Protocol 1 is depicted in Figure 5a. It was observed that *E. coli* initial concentration affected the number of CFU on the substrate i.e., the higher the initial concentration the higher the number of CFU. However, as porosity increased (fully-dense vs. porous c.p. Ti) the number of CFU was significantly increased, especially at the lowest initial bacteria concentration (C3). *E. coli* bacteria concentration of the medium could influence the medium-substrate interaction. After incubating the samples for 1 h at 37 °C, the number of CFU in the corresponding solutions was determined by membrane filtration. Protocol 2 revealed no bacteria attached onto the flat surface. By Protocol 3, bacteria inside the pores was quantified and its normalization by the surface is shown in Figure 5b,c, respectively. As the size of the spacer increased the number of CFU also increased at both initial bacteria concentrations (Figure 5b).

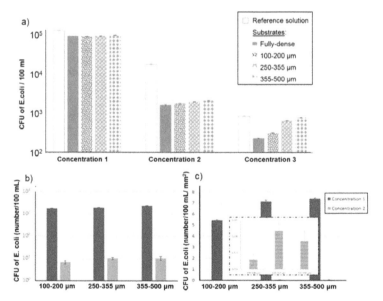

Figure 5. Bacteria quantification following protocols described (P1, P2, and P3). (**a**) CFU of *E. coli* bacteria after membrane filtration (Protocol 1), CFU of *E. coli* bacteria inside the pores measured following Protocol 3: (**b**) absolute values and (**c**) normalized values by the inner pores surface. Inset: magnification view of the concentration view for the normalized values.

3.4. In Vitro Cell Studies

The different studied substrates were tested in vitro conditions using two murine cell lines. In first place, C2C12-GFP premioblastic line was used to evaluate the process of cell adhesion and proliferation after 1, 4, 7, and 10 days of cell culture compiling the results in Figure 6. C2C12-GFP cells were capable to attach and proliferate over the surface and inside the pores, increasing the cell density presented on the samples over time. In the first 24 h, the inverted fluorescence images showed similar cell density between fully-dense and porous substrates. After 4 days, several small green dots which correspond to small alive cell clusters were observed totally dispersed on the surface. Furthermore, at longer incubation periods, cells were able to proliferate, showing an increased cell density over the entire surface. Indeed, at day 10 C2C12 GFP cells were covering the entire porous structure, even filling the pores attaching on pore's walls and arriving to the edge of the samples (see Figure 7 after 10 days, 255–350 µm sample). Figure 7 showed a higher magnification of C2C12-GFP cells growing at 4 days to analyze the cell morphology on c.p. Ti samples. A clear different cell shape was observed between cells growing on flat surfaces and inside pores. Premioblastic cells growing on fully-dense samples showed fusiform morphology, with an elongated cell shape. This cell morphology, most frequent of fibroblastic phenotype, was also observed in flat surfaces of porous substrates independently of pore size (see Figure 7).

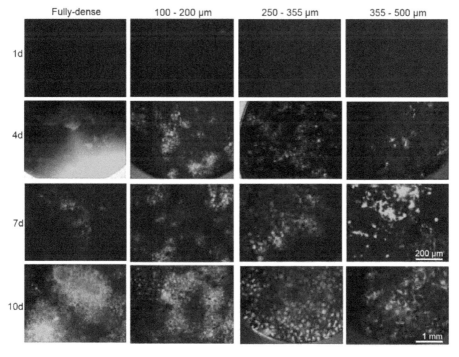

Figure 6. Inverted fluorescence microphotographs of cell adhesion and proliferation of C2C12-GFP cells after 1, 4, 7, and 10 days of cell culture. Common scale bar, 1mm, except for 7 days and pore size 355–500 µm, which a specific scale bar is indicated (200 µm).

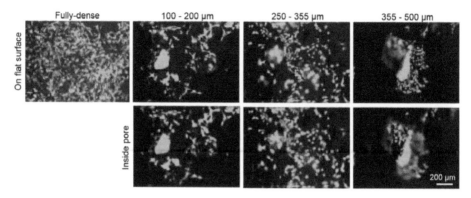

Figure 7. Higher magnification of microphotographs of C2C12-GFP cells growing after day 4 of cell incubation. Common scale bar.

Cell viability determination was performed after 4 days using osteoblast cells and the results were compiled in Figure 8. Cell viability was expressed as percentage of fully dense samples, showing an increased cell viability of osteoblast growing on the three porous structures compared to the control surface (fully-dense). Although cell viability results are slightly higher for porous samples respect to fully-dense substrates, this observed trend was not statistically significant and, therefore, no differences in cell viability could be observed between surfaces ($p > 0.05$).

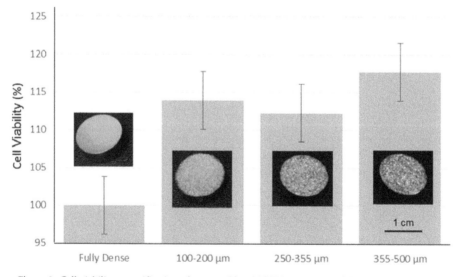

Figure 8. Cell viability quantification of preosteoblast MC3T3 growing on fully-dense and porous substrates after 4 days of cell incubation. Percentages of cell viability are coupled with representative images from a macroscopic point of view. No statistics differences were observed between surfaces ($p > 0.05$), however, porous substrates reached higher percentages than the control fully-dense surface. Common scale bar for all the images.

Figure 9 presents the images of preosteoblast MC3T3E1 cell cytoskeleton morphology, showing actin fibers (in red) and cell nuclei of stained osteoblast (in blue) after 10 days of cell culture. Firstly, it was observed that, the entire surface of fully-dense and porous substrates was completely covered by osteoblast. Some flat areas in samples prepared with higher space-holder particles size (355–500 µm) were not totally covered and a heterogeneous random distribution was observed compared to the homogeneous cell spread of osteoblast in the other three surfaces. Images on the middle and bottom depict porous structures in Figure 9 corresponds to a higher magnification area (using 10× and 20× lenses). These micro-photographs showed the same area with focusing in two different points, on flat surface and inside pores. As it is shown, the cell nuclei of MC3T3E1 cells in the three porous substrates were covering the total flat surface exposed and the elongated actin fibers connecting between cells almost producing a cell sheet. In contrast, fully-dense surfaces revealed more than one cell monolayer growing on top of another cell sheet. This situation might reduce the corresponding cell viability of the cell culture and promote the detachment of the cell sheet.

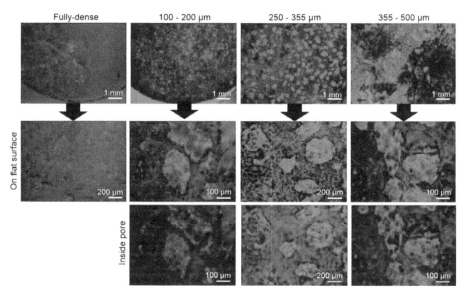

Figure 9. Immunofluorescence images of cell actin cytoskeleton (in red) and cell nuclei (in blue) of preosteoblast MC3T3 growing for 10 days. Medium and lower images correspond to higher magnification of areas focusing in same area on flat and inside pores of the studied specimens. Bottom images show the cells attached inside pores and medium the same cells well focused on flat areas.

4. Discussion

As it is shown in the optical microscopy images (Figure 3), all porous c.p. Ti substrates present two different ranges of pore sizes; pores with a size below 50 μm were generated during the sintering process. In addition, they are not critical in mechanical and biological behavior of the substrates. Otherwise, the larger pores correspond to the former spacer particles, showing a D_{eq} in the range of the size of these particles (161.1 ± 28.5 μm for 100–200, 261.5 ± 9.0 μm for 250–355, and 293.4 ± 28.2 μm for the 355–500 μm of the spacer particles size, as it was determined by IA). Porosity results obtained by the different techniques (Table 1) differ due to the inherent characteristics of them: Archimedes' is a volumetric method, IA analysis is superficial while M-CT only takes into account a volumetric fraction of the sample. The total porosity is slightly below the expected 50%. Nevertheless, different factors can influence. For instance, remaining small amount of undissolved NH_4HCO_3, which are enclosed in the isolated pores, and the slight reduction of the volume associated with the space-holder during sintering would contribute to reduce the porosity while an increase on the porosity could be also expected because of the additional micro-pores generated during the sintering.

Total inner surface has been calculated analyzing a M-CT representative fraction of total sample volume. The lowest value was obtained for the intermediate size 255–350 μm (260.1 ± 29.6 mm^2), while similar values were calculated for the other samples (321.0 ± 44.8 and 311.9 ± 29.9 for 100–200 μm and 350–500 μm, respectively). Similarly, roughness quantification by the analysis of confocal microscopy images revealed an increased roughness in porous surfaces compared to flat surface, as it has been described above.

Concerning the pores, D_{eq}, analyzed by IA and M-CT (see Table 2), a similar tendency was observed for both techniques. In the case of IA, also information about the shape factor has been obtained, revealing high symmetry of the pores, since it is close to one for all the substrates. By M-CT, the roughness has been analyzed (Table 2), the higher pore size (355–500 μm), the smoother surface. Roughness improves cellular adhesion [3,5], so it is desirable for osseointegration; however, depending on the roughness values it can affect bacteria adhesion.

Additionally, the mechanical behavior of the substrate is an important feature since the ideal implant should be mechanically similar to the bone. The mechanical properties of the fully-dense substrates are far from those of cortical bone tissues. However, all porous substrates present a Young's modulus similar to the one of the cortical bone [25]. The yield strength values of the porous samples are lower than that of the bone, but they remain closer to the ideal values compared with fully-dense substrates [26].

Microhardness has been evaluated by two load levels that reveal different results: HV0.3 and HV1 (Table 3). Comparing the results, the differences in terms of applied load for one substrate could be related to the localized microplasticity phenomena and indentation size effects. The microhardness and the local stiffness of the porous c.p. Ti substrates depend on the remaining material and the surrounding pores (size and distribution). For low load (HV0.3), the microhardness of porous substrates and fully-dense samples is similar due to the Ti matrix remaining sufficiently large between the pores (i.e., no porosity influence). However, for higher load (HV1), an effect of the pore and porosity on the micro-mechanical behavior (material collapse, buckling, etc.) can be appreciated. The pore size influences the microhardness in an opposite way, it means, the samples with a higher pore size present a lower microhardness value due to the larger area of the Ti-matrix among the pores. However, a detailed study may be required to determine the main influential parameters to the results as the mean free path between pores and the number of indentations.

Once the mechanical properties have evaluated, next the bio-functional behavior is studied. Following Protocol 1, the bacteria concentration of the medium was measured. As it is shown in Figure 5a, both fully-dense and porous substrates inhibited the bacterial growth for the three studied concentrations compared to the reference solution (bacteria only). This reduction was particularly significant for fully-dense c.p. Ti substrates and lower initial bacteria concentrations (C3) while for bacteria solution (C1), the substrate influence was irrelevant. This difference between the fully-dense and the porous samples can be explained by two possible factors: the growth rate is higher for lower bacteria concentrations in the media, achieving a stationary state and/or higher concentrations of bacteria mean that the bacteria thronged the cavities, hampering penetration into the pore.

Measurements obtained by Protocol 2 for the *E. coli* strain showed no bacteria growth and adhesion onto the flat surfaces. For the porous samples, the flat surface corresponds to the polished c.p. Ti matrix surface that remains among all the pores. After incubating the Petri dish where the swab was smeared, no bacteria grew. For this same strain, Protocol 3 revealed bacterial presence inside the pores (Figure 5). This difference in terms of behavior between the two surfaces could be related to the micro-roughness pattern of the porous surface. A similar pattern has been reported for osteoblasts [4,5]. As it is shown in Figure 5b, the number of CFU inside the pores was larger for porous substrates with larger pore size and at higher concentrations. A higher initial bacteria concentration implies higher probability of bacteria attaching inside the pores. The influence of the pore size could be ignored compared to the effect of the concentration for absolute values. Nevertheless, once the number of CFU was adjusted in relation to the area (Figure 5c), it was relatively insignificant.

To compare the bacteria behavior and the studied substrates different factors have been considered. On the one hand, the presence of pores and, on the other hand, the real surface, which is related to pores inner roughness. In this context, it has been observed that the presence of pores promote bacteria proliferation. Otherwise, normalized values by real surface area reveals that the value was not higher than expected. Pore number, size, shape, and surface roughness inside the pores are also relevant. At higher pore size (368.4 ± 9.1 µm) as measured by M-CT, more bacteria are adhered into them. In contrast, bigger pores present smoother walls (3.3 ± 0.6 µm), which would make more difficult the bacteria adhesion. However, the obtained results for this bacteria strain show that pore size is more significant than roughness.

Regarding the behavior of mammalian cells such as myoblast or osteoblast cell lines, several studies have been performed. Cell viability, adhesion, proliferation, and differentiation of osteoblast are key factors for bone tissue reconstruction purposes [27] and these processes can be influenced by tailoring the surface properties of the medical device such as hydrophilicity, roughness, pore size, morphology, and distribution. Pore size is one key parameter that has been deeply reported in several studies suggesting pore size between 20 µm to 500 µm are appropriate for bone regeneration [28]. These values covered a wide range of pore sizes, however, if the pores are quite small, the blood vessel network cannot exchange nutrients and oxygen to new bone tissue. Conversely, if the pore is too large, the mechanical properties may compromise the internal stability of the implant. Although the most suitable pore size for bone regeneration process is still controversial, for Ti implants a pore range from 150 to 500 µm has been established, taking into account the role of the interconnected pores in the proper development of the new vascularization system [29]. During the course of this study, all porous surfaces showed a non-toxic behavior and a good cell adhesion for C2C12GFP achieving similar cell density after 24 h compared to the fully-dense control surface (Figure 6). In fact, the presence of cells attached on the surface on all c.p. Ti substrates serves as an indicative factor of biocompatibility of the manufacturing process of porous structures by powder metallurgy and space-holder techniques which have been previously described as safety technologies to develop non-toxic 3D porous structures [30].

Even though the cell density attached on the surface after day 1 is low, C2C12GFP cells could proliferate and grew further after 4, 7, and 10 days, increasing the cell density, which was observed as a higher fluorescence intensity signal (Figure 6). After 4 days, C2C12-GFP density increased compared to day 1. However, premioblastic cells grew in clusters randomly dispersed, leaving flat areas empty without cells attached on the surface. This behavior evolved, and after day 7, a continuous cell monolayer was developed covering the center and, in some cases, reaching the edges of the c.p. Ti samples, and thus, reducing the flat areas with no cells attached. Some pores were covered by osteoblast after 10 days which appeared as intense green fluorescence signal. Here, many areas were totally covered, including flat and inside pores, in which cells were expanded and connected forming a cell monolayer. At this time, the presence of pores offers a different surface (increased roughness values and surface contact area) which may allow the proper growth of both myofibroblast/osteoblast and *E. coli* as we have previously described. In case of fully-dense surfaces, the presence of more than one cell monolayer could reduce the cell viability, but bacteria may take advantage and spread and migrate to new sites over the medical implant.

Several authors have reported that the presence of pores (and their size, morphology, roughness, and interconnectivity), the surface chemistry, and surface free energy of metallic based biomaterials have a strong influence on the initial adhesion and early differentiation of osteoblast lineage cells [31–33]. Although the aim of this study was to evaluate the bacteria behavior on porous c.p. Ti structure compared to cell adhesion and proliferation of in vitro cell lines, both C2C12GFP and MC3T3 cells shared some similar points. Firstly, both cell lines were able to attach and proliferate confirming the cell viability values of osteoblast which were higher on porous surfaces over the samples after 4 days (see Figure 8). Even where there were not statistically differences on cell viability, the three porous c.p. Ti substrates achieved higher percentages than control fully-dense surface (113.89%, 112.28%, 117.74%, and 100%, respectively). The larger pore size, 355–500 µm, offered higher cell viability percentage which was also correlated to the higher attached *E. coli*, confirming the higher pore surfaces structure as an advance surface to promote cellular and bacteria adhesion.

Secondly, the specific tailored microstructure of porous scaffolds by space-holder have a strong impact on cell adhesion which one can observe in the differential cell morphology showed in Figures 7 and 9. The cell morphology of osteoblasts is usually a response to the surface properties of the inner material. Inside the pores, osteoblast cells showed a more cuboidal cell cytoskeleton compared to a more fusiform cell shape on flat surfaces (either fully-dense or flat surface of porous c.p. Ti samples). This distinction in cell morphology can be correlated to an advanced cell adhesion state which also can affect other cellular processes such as osteoblast cell differentiation growing inside pores as it was described in the literature [33].

Some reports have described the influence of surface properties on cell morphology and how the shape of the cells is also connected with other cellular functions such as cell adhesion, proliferation, differentiation, and mineralization processes [34,35]. Furthermore, the increased inner roughness values of pores compared to flat surface (of fully-dense or even flat surface of porous samples) has been described as a key factor for osteoblast adhesion and differentiation studied [5,33]. Inside the pores, osteoblast cells attached on the wall perceive higher load transfer and this local stress will promote cell differentiation and mineralization, and therefore, the need for bone ingrowth [33]. However, these cells growing inside pores presented a different cell morphology, revealing a more cuboidal structure, round shape, and less elongation.

The cell morphology observed inside the pores could be related to an advance cell adhesion, being the 100–200 μm porous substrate the best pore size to promote cellular adhesion and reduced bacteria attachment compared to larger pore size 355–500 μm and fully-dense substrates.

5. Conclusions

The microstructural parameters of titanium porous samples fabricated by space-holder technique are consistent with the initial design criteria (characteristics of the spacer holder particles: volume fraction and size range), supporting the viability and reliability of this economic route of manufacturing substrates with controlled porosity. The porous substrates obtained with this technique, in the range of 100–200 μm, presented the best mechanical balance (higher Young's modulus, yield strength, and microhardness). Besides, this substrate also revealed the highest interconnected porosity, potentially improving the bone in-growth. It is worth to highlight that both, spacer particle size and pores inner surface topography, have a strong influence on adhesion of osteoblasts and bacteria proliferation (*E. coli* strain). However, the results revealed that the predominant parameter in bacteria behavior is pore morphology (equivalent diameter). Therefore, the bigger pore size showed higher bacteria attachment. To summarize, substrates with smaller pore sizes can be considered the most suitable, since this range of pore sizes can assure the best biomechanical, cellular, and antibacterial behavior.

Author Contributions: Conceptualization, project administration, supervision J.A.R.-O. and Y.T; Investigation, formal analysis, validation A.C., A.M.B., C.D.-T., M.D.G, J.L., F.G.M., J.V.C.-R., and J.J.G.; Discussion and writing—original draft preparation, all authors.

Funding: This research was funded by the Ministry of Economy and Competitiveness of Spain under the grant MAT2015-71284-P and of the Junta de Andalucía—FEDER (Spain) through the project ref. P12-TEP-1401.

Acknowledgments: The authors dedicate this paper to the memory of Juan J. Pavón Palacio (University of Antioquia, Colombia). Authors thank to A. S., C. L., and M.V.S. for experimental work for bacteria studies. The authors would like to thank J. Pinto for assistance in micro-mechanical testing. AMB also thanks the financial support of the University of Seville for the research stay at Institute of Applied Materials, Helmholtz-Zentrum Berlin für Materialien und Energie, Berlin (Germany) (Grant: VI Plan Propio de Investigación y Transferencia—US 2018, I.3A2).

Conflicts of Interest: The authors declare no conflict of interest.

References

1. Kunčická, N.; Kocich, R.; Lowe, T.C. Advances in metals and alloys for joint replacement. *Prog. Mater. Sci.* **2017**, *88*, 232–280. [CrossRef]
2. Niinomi, M. Mechanical biocompatibilities of titanium alloys for biomedical applications. *J. Mech. Behav. Biomed. Mater.* **2008**, *1*, 30–42. [CrossRef] [PubMed]
3. Torres, Y.; Pavón, J.J.; Rodríguez-Ortiz, J.A. Processing and characterization of porous titanium for implants by using NaCl as space holder. *J. Mater. Process. Technol.* **2012**, *212*, 1061–1069. [CrossRef]
4. Torres, Y.; Pavón, J.J.; Nieto, I.; Rodríguez-Ortiz, J.A. Conventional powder metallurgy process and characterization of porous titanium for biomedical applications. *Metall. Mater. Trans. B Process Metall. Mater. Process. Sci.* **2011**, *42*, 891–900. [CrossRef]
5. Muñoz, S.; Pavón, J.J.; Rodríguez-Ortiz, J.A.; Civantos, A.; Allain, J.P.; Torres, Y. On the influence of space holder in the development of porous titanium implants: Mechanical, computational and biological evaluation. *Mater. Charact.* **2015**, *108*, 68–78. [CrossRef]
6. Jurczyk, M.U.; Jurczyk, K.; Miklaszewski, A.; Jurczyk, M. Nanostructured titanium-45S5 Bioglass scaffold composites for medical applications. *Mater. Des.* **2011**, *32*, 4882–4889. [CrossRef]
7. Trueba, P. Desarrollo de Titanio con Porosidad Gradiente Radial y Longitudinal para Aplicaciones Biomédicas. Ph.D. Thesis, University of Seville, Seville, Spain, 2017.
8. Naebe, M.; Shirvanimoghaddam, K. Functionally graded materials: A review of fabrication and properties. *Appl. Mater. Today* **2016**, *5*, 223–245. [CrossRef]
9. Sola, A.; Belluci, D.; Cannillo, V. Functionally graded materials for orthopedic applications—An update on design and manufacturing. *Biotechnol. Adv.* **2016**, *34*, 504–531. [CrossRef] [PubMed]
10. Singh, S.; Ramakrishna, S.; Singh, R. Material issues in additive manufacturing: A review. *J. Manuf. Process.* **2017**, *25*, 185–200. [CrossRef]
11. Jha, N.; Mondal, D.P.; Majumdar, J.D.; Badkul, A.; Jha, A.K.; Khare, A.K. Highly porous open cell Ti-foam using NaCl as temporary space holder through powder metallurgy route. *Mater. Des.* **2013**, *47*, 810–819. [CrossRef]
12. Torres, Y.; Pavón, J.J.; Trueba, P.; Cobos, J.; Rodriguez-Ortiz, J.A. Design, fabrication and characterization of titanium with graded porosity by using space-holder technique. *Procedia Mater. Sci.* **2014**, *4*, 115–119. [CrossRef]
13. Jakubowicz, J.; Adamek, G.; Dewidar, M. Titanium foam made with saccharose as a space holder. *J. Porous Mater.* **2013**, *20*, 1137–1141. [CrossRef]
14. Dominguez-Trujillo, C.; Ternero, F.; Rodriguez-Ortiz, J.A.; Pavón, J.J.; García-Couce, J.; Galvan, J.C.; García-Moreno, F.; Torres, Y. Improvement of the balance between a reduced stress shielding and bone ingrowth by bioactive coatings onto porous titanium substrates. *Surf. Coat. Technol.* **2018**, *338*, 32–37. [CrossRef]
15. Esen, Z.; Bor, Ş. Processing of titanium foams using magnesium spacer particles. *Scr. Mater.* **2007**, *56*, 341–344. [CrossRef]
16. Vlacic-Zischke, J.; Hamle, S.M.; Friis, T.; Tonetti, M.S.; Ivanovski, S. The influence of surface microroughness and hydrophilicity of titanium on the up-regulation of TGFβ/BMP signalling in osteoblasts. *Biomaterials* **2011**, *32*, 665–671. [CrossRef] [PubMed]
17. Civantos, A.; Martinez-Campos, E.; Ramos, V.; Elvira, C.; Gallardo, A.; Abarrategi, A. Titanium coatings and surface modifications: Toward clinically useful bioactive implants. *ACS Biomater. Sci. Eng.* **2017**, *3*, 1245–1261. [CrossRef]
18. Gristina, A.G. Biomaterial-centered infection: Microbial adhesion versus tissue integration. *Science* **1987**, *237*, 1588–1595. [CrossRef]
19. Neoh, K.G.; Hu, X.; Zheng, D.; Kang, E.T. Balancing osteoblast functions and bacterial adhesion on functionalized titanium surfaces. *Biomaterials* **2012**, *33*, 2813–2822. [CrossRef]
20. Tuson, H.H.; Auer, G.K.; Renner, L.D.; Hasebe, M.; Tropini, C.; Salick, M.; Weibel, D.B. Measuring the stiffness of bacterial cells from growth rates in hydrogels of tunable elasticity. *Mol. Microbiol.* **2012**, *84*, 874–891. [CrossRef]

21. Dominguez-Trujillo, C.; Beltrán, A.M.; Garvi, M.D.; Salazar-Moya, A.; Lebrato, J.; Hickey, D.J.; Rodriguez-Ortiz, J.A.; Kamm, P.H.; Lebrato, C.; García-Moreno, F.; et al. Bacterial behavior on coated porous titanium substrate for biomedical applications. *Surf. Coat. Technol.* **2019**, *357*, 896–902. [CrossRef]

22. García-Moreno, F.; Fromme, M.; Banhart, J. Real-time X-ray radioscopy on metallic foams using a compact micro-focus source. *Adv. Eng. Mater.* **2004**, *6*, 416–420. [CrossRef]

23. AENOR. *Water Quality—Detection and Enumeration of Escherichia coli and Coliform Bacteria—Part 1: Membrane Filtration Method*; UNE-EN ISO 9308-1:2014; International Organization for Standardization: Geneva, Switzerland, 2014.

24. *Sterilization of Medical Devices—Microbiological Methods Part 1: Determination of a Population of Microorganisms on Products*; ISO 11737:1:2007; International Organization for Standardization: Geneva, Switzerland, 2017.

25. Grimal, Q.; Haupert, S.; Mitton, D.; Vastel, L.; Laugier, P. Assessment of cortical bone elasticity and strength: Mechanical testing and ultrasound provide complementary data. *Med. Eng. Phys.* **2009**, *31*, 1140–1147. [CrossRef] [PubMed]

26. Hasan, J.; Crawford, R.J.; Ivanova, E.P. Antibacterial surfaces: The quest for a new generation of biomaterials. *Trends Biotechnol.* **2013**, *31*, 295–304. [CrossRef] [PubMed]

27. St-Pierre, J.P.; Gauthier, M.; Lefebvre, L.P.; Tabrizian, M. Three-dimensional growth of differentiating MC3T3-E1 pre-osteoblasts on porous titanium scaffolds. *Biomaterials* **2005**, *26*, 7319–7328. [CrossRef] [PubMed]

28. Murphy, C.M.; O'Brien, F.J. Understanding the effect of mean pore size on cell activity in collagen-glycosaminoglycan scaffolds. *Cell Adhes. Migr.* **2010**, *4*, 377–381. [CrossRef] [PubMed]

29. do Prado, R.F.; de Oliveira, F.S.; Nascimento, R.D.; de Vasconcellos, L.M.R.; Carvalho, Y.R.; Cairo, C.A.A. Osteoblast response to porous titanium and biomimetic surface: In vitro analysis. *Mater. Sci. Eng. C* **2015**, *52*, 194–203. [CrossRef] [PubMed]

30. Wang, D.; Li, Q.; Xu, M.; Jiang, G.; Zhang, Y.; He, G. A novel approach to fabrication of three-dimensional porous titanium with controllable structure. *Mater. Sci. Eng. C* **2017**, *71*, 1046–1051. [CrossRef] [PubMed]

31. Chang, M.C.; Tsai, Y.L.; Liou, E.J.W.; Tang, C.M.; Wang, T.M.; Liu, H.C.; Liao, M.W.; Yeung, S.Y.; Chan, C.P.; Jeng, J.H. Effect of Butyrate on Collagen Expression, Cell Viability, Cell Cycle Progression and Related Proteins Expression of MG-63 Osteoblastic Cells. *PLoS ONE* **2016**, *11*, e0165438. [CrossRef] [PubMed]

32. Chen, X.; Zhi, X.; Wang, J.; Su, J.C. RANKL signaling in bone marrow mesenchymal stem cells negatively regulates osteoblastic bone formation. *Bone Res.* **2018**, *6*, 34. [CrossRef]

33. Civantos, A.; Domínguez, C.; Pino, R.J.; Setti, G.; Pavon, J.J.; Martínez-Campos, E.; Garcia-Garcia, F.J.; Rodriguez-Ortiz, J.A.; Allain, J.P.; Torres, Y. Designing bioactive porous titanium interfaces to balance mechanical properties and in vitro cells behavior towards increased osseointegration. *Surf. Coat. Technol.* **2019**, *368*, 162–174. [CrossRef]

34. Kamada, R.; Tano, F.; Kudoh, F.; Kimura, N.; Chuman, Y.; Osawa, A.; Namba, K.; Tanino, K.; Sakaguchi, K. Effective Cellular Morphology Analysis for Differentiation Processes by a Fluorescent 1,3a,6a-Triazapentalene Derivative Probe in Live Cells. *PLoS ONE* **2016**, *11*, e0160625. [CrossRef] [PubMed]

35. Hong, D.; Chen, H.X.; Yu, H.Q.; Liang, Y.; Wang, C.; Lian, Q.Q.; Deng, H.T.; Ge, R.S. Morphological and proteomic analysis of early stage of osteoblast differentiation in osteoblastic progenitor cells. *Exp. Cell Res.* **2010**, *316*, 2291–2300. [CrossRef] [PubMed]

Article

Microstructure of a V-Containing Cobalt Based Alloy Prepared by Mechanical Alloying and Hot Pressed Sintering

Niannian Li [1], Fengshi Yin [2],* and Liu Feng [3],*

[1] School of Chemical Engineering, Shandong University of Technology, Zibo 255049, China; niannianli0708@163.com
[2] School of Mechanical Engineering, Shandong University of Technology, Zibo 255049, China
[3] Analysis & Testing Center, Shandong University of Technology, Zibo 255049, China
*   Correspondence: fsyin@sdut.edu.cn (F.Y.); willow-feng@163.com (L.F.);
    Tel.: +86-1360-533-1243 (F.Y.); +86-1358-949-8883 (L.F.)

Received: 8 March 2019; Accepted: 16 April 2019; Published: 22 April 2019

Abstract: In this paper, a bulk V-containing cobalt-based alloy with high chromium and tungsten contents was prepared by mechanical alloying and hot pressed sintering using Co, Cr, W, Ni, V and C pure element powders. XRD, SEM, TEM and Vickers hardness tests were employed to characterize the microstructure and mechanical properties of the mechanical alloyed powders and hot pressed bulk cobalt-based alloy. The results show that all elements can be mixed uniformly and that the Co, Cr, and Ni elements were made into an amorphous state after 10 h ball milling in a high energy ball miller. The microstructure of the prepared bulk alloy was composed of a γ-Co matrix with a large number of nano-twins and fine $M_{23}C_6$ and $M_{12}C$ carbide particles well-distributed in the alloy. The V element was mainly distributed in $M_{23}C_6$-type carbide and no V-rich MC-type carbide was found in the microstructure. The prepared alloy had a high hardness of 960 ± 9.2 HV and good a fracture toughness K_{Ic} of about 10.5 ± 0.46 MPa·m$^{1/2}$. The microstructure formation and strengthening mechanisms of the prepared cobalt-based alloy are discussed.

Keywords: cobalt-based alloy; mechanical alloying; hot pressed sintering; microstructure

---

1. Introduction

Stellite alloys, a kind of Co-based alloys, are very important in the development of science, technology, and the progress of industry. They are mainly composed of carbon, cobalt, chromium, tungsten, molybdenum, etc. Metal carbides formed in the alloy are used as hard phases and Co as the matrix bonding phase [1,2]. Stellite alloys are widely used industries such as aerospace, nuclear, mining machinery, and material machining due to their characteristics of wear-resistance, high temperature resistance, high strength, high hardness, and a certain toughness. In order to further increase the wear-resistant properties, Tribaloy alloy, another kind of Co-based alloys, which contains a large volume fraction of intermetallic Laves phases in γ-Co matrix, has been developed [3,4]. It is the presence of this large volume fraction of Laves phases that enables these materials to resist wear under poor or unlubricated conditions.

Typically, cobalt-based alloys are prepared by casting or powder metallurgy technology. The casting process is simple in terms of the technology needed and low in cost, but the size and distribution of carbides are strongly dependent on the casting temperature of the melt, cooling rate, and thermal treatment condition, which must be strictly controlled to avoid defects such as macro-segregation, micro-segregation, porosity, solidification shrinkage, and second phase inclusions [5,6]. Cobalt-based alloys can be also manufactured by powder metallurgy process using pre-alloyed powders [7,8].

However, chemical element segregation and oxidation will occur on the surface of the pre-alloyed powders, which introduces the prior particle boundary (PPB), and therefore, decreases the mechanical properties of the final powder metallurgy product [9]. Mechanical alloying (MA) [10–12] and hot pressed sintering, as another powder metallurgy technology, have the potential to shorten the whole preparing period and produce bulk materials with a uniform fine-grained microstructure. The as-prepared materials exhibit excellent properties such as high density, good hot workability and improved mechanical properties.

It is well known that vanadium is a strong carbide-forming element and vanadium-containing high speed steel W18Cr4V has a good wear-resistant property. However, there is no report about the effect of vanadium on cobalt-based alloys. Berthod [13] reported a TiC carbide containing cobalt-based alloy. In this work, based on the Stellite alloys, we designed a novel vanadium-containing cobalt-based alloy with high chromium and tungsten contents. The alloy was prepared using MA and vacuum hot pressed sintering methods aiming to further increase the wear-resistant property of cobalt-based alloy. The microstructure and mechanical properties of the mechanically alloyed powders and hot pressed bulk cobalt-based alloy was characterized.

2. Materials and Methods

The cobalt-based alloy with a nominal composition of Co-32.4%, Cr-32%, W-25%, Ni-5%, V-5%, and C-0.6% (in wt. %) was prepared by mechanical alloying and hot pressing using pure element powders of Co, Cr, W, Ni, V, and C. The purity of these elemental powders was greater than 99.5%. The process of mechanical alloying was carried out in a high energy ball mill (SPEX8000D, SPEX SamplePrep, Metuchen, NJ, USA) using a stainless-steel vial and stainless-steel balls of 7 mm in diameter. The ratio of ball to powder was 10:1 in weight. The 5 wt. % ethanol was used as the process control agent during the ball milling process. The volume of the vial was 56 mL. A 10 g mixture of the powders with the stainless-steel balls was charged into the stainless-steel vial under high pure argon atmosphere. The ball milled powders were put into a graphite mold and sintered in a vacuum hot press sintering furnace (ZRY-30L, Jinzhou Hangxing Vacuum Equipment Co., Ltd., Jinzhou, China). After the furnace was evacuated using a vacuum pump to 10 Pa and then heated to 1200 °C at a heating rate of 4 °C/min, the ball milled powders were sintered at a pressure of 60 MPa for 20 min and cooled in the furnace. The ball milled powders and hot pressed bulk sample were examined by X-ray diffraction with Cu Kα radiation (XRD, Bruker AXS D8 Advance, Bruker AXS GmbH, Karlsruhe, Germany), a scanning electron microscope (SEM, FEI Quanta 250, FEI, Hillsboro, OR, USA), and a transmission electron microscope (TEM, FEI Tecnai G2 F20, FEI, Hillsboro, OR, USA) equipped with energy dispersive X-ray spectrometry (EDS, EDAX Apollo) and a scanning transmission electron microscope mode (STEM). Quantitative metallography was used to measure the volume fraction and particle size of various phases in the microstructures of the obtained alloy. The TEM samples were prepared by an ion thinning instrument (Gantan 695.C, Gatan, Inc., Pleasanton, CA, USA). The hardness of the hot pressed bulk sample was measured by a Vickers hardness tester (Laizhou Huayin Testing Instrument Co., Ltd., Laizhou, China) using a 5 kgf load. Fracture toughness was determined according to the hardness indentation method. Five measurements were used to calculate average value of hardness and toughness.

3. Results

Figure 1 shows the XRD patterns of the powders ball milled with various time. It can be seen that at the initial state, the diffraction peaks of Co, Cr, W, and Ni are clearly shown in the pattern, while the corresponding diffraction peaks of C and V were not present due to their low content. The diffraction intensity of all elements decreased gradually with the milling time. The diffraction peaks of Co, Cr, and Ni elements almost disappear except for the W element after 10 h milling. No obvious change was seen upon further milling for up to 30 h, but peak broadening of W elements was observed. The disappearance of the diffraction peaks of Co, Cr, and Ni elements indicates that these element powders were transformed into an amorphous state. The XRD peak broadening reveals that the W powders had been transformed into a nanocrystalline state. The crystallite size of the W powders after milling 10 and 30 h, estimated using the Scherrer formula [14], was found to be approximately 25 and 17 nm, respectively.

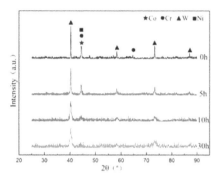

Figure 1. X-ray diffraction patterns of the powders ball milled for different time.

The morphology and micro-structural details of the milled powders were investigated by SEM. Figure 2 shows the SEM images for the powders ball milled for 10 h. The milled powders had an irregular morphology with a size below 15 μm. A local amplified back-scattered electron (BSE) image (Figure 2b) of one particle shows that some white particles about 30 nm in size are distributed uniformly in the powders. According to the XRD results of the milled powders (Figure 1), the white particles were deduced to be W phase. The element mapping image (Figure 2c) of EDS reveals that all elements had been mixed uniformly after 10 h ball milling.

Figure 2. SEM images of the cobalt-based alloy powders after milling for 10 h, (**a**) morphology of the milled powders, (**b**) back-scattered electron (BSE) image of one particle, and (**c**) element mapping image of energy dispersive X-ray spectrometry (EDS) results.

The cobalt-based alloy powders milled for 10 h were selected for vacuum hot pressed sintering in the subsequent experiment. Figure 3 is the SEM-BSE image of the obtained bulk cobalt-based alloy showing that there were three kinds of phases in the alloy according to the contrast, i.e., bright, grey, and dark phases. XRD results (Figure 4) of the obtained bulk cobalt-based alloy show that these three phases were $M_{12}C$ (Co_6W_6C, JCPDS 22-0597), γ-Co (JCPDS 15-0806) matrix, and $M_{23}C_6$ ($Cr_{23}C_6$, JCPDS 85-01281), respectively, all of which had a cubic structure. According to the XRD results, the lattice constants of $M_{12}C$, γ-Co and $M_{23}C_6$ were 1.0922, 0.3552, and 1.0657 nm, respectively. No PPBs were found (Figure 3) in the prepared alloy by hot pressed sintering using mechanical alloyed powders. Figure 5 is STEM high-angle annular dark field (HAADF) image and selected area electron diffraction (SAED) patterns of the phases with different morphology and contrast. Both the STEM-HAADF and SEM-BSE images are atomic number contrast (Z-contrast) images, the γ-Co matrix, M_6C, and $M_{23}C_6$ phases have similar contrast in Figures 3 and 5. Table 1 summarizes the STEM-EDS results and identified phases by SAED patterns for the phases labeled in Figure 5a. Fe in EDS results would have been introduced from stainless-steel vial and balls during mechanical alloying process. According to the results mentioned above, we can conclude that the bright phase was W-containing $M_{12}C$ carbide in which lots of Cr and V atoms dissolved, the grey phase is the γ-Co matrix, and the dark phase was Cr and V-rich $M_{23}C_6$ carbide. The V element was mainly distributed in $M_{23}C_6$-type carbide and no V-rich MC-type (M indicates metal elements) carbide was found in the obtained alloy. The $M_{12}C$-type carbide particles had a size of about 1 μm dispersed in the γ-Co matrix. Some coarse $M_{23}C_6$-type carbide particles have a strip-like shape with about 1 μm in length dispersed in the γ-Co matrix and some fine $M_{23}C_6$-type carbide particles with about 200 nm in length present within both the γ-Co matrix and $M_{12}C$-type carbide. The volume fraction of $M_{12}C$ and $M_{23}C_6$ phases were determined to be about 19.4% and 11.95%, respectively, by using quantitative metallography.

Figure 3. SEM back-scattered electron image of the obtained bulk cobalt-based alloy.

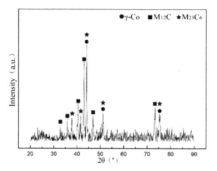

Figure 4. XRD result of the obtained bulk cobalt-based alloy.

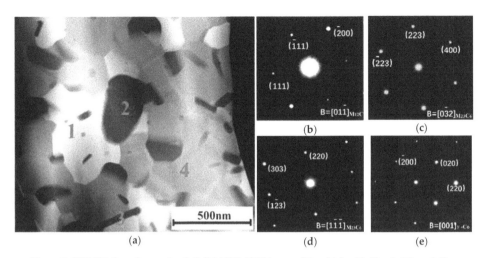

Figure 5. STEM high-angle annular dark field (HAADF) image of the obtained bulk cobalt-based alloy (a) and selected area electron diffraction (SAED) patterns of the different phases labeled in (a), (b) point 1, bright, (c) point 2, dark, (d) point 3, dark, and (e) point 4, grey.

Table 1. STEM-EDS results of the phases in the prepared bulk cobalt-based alloy (at. %).

Point	Cr	W	V	Ni	Co	Fe	C	Phase
1 (bright)	29.93	16.44	8.11	0	31.40	2.11	12.01	$M_{12}C$
2 (dark)	50.46	0	23.38	0	0	0	21.52	$M_{23}C_6$
3 (dark)	53.08	0	26.07	0	0	0.70	17.39	$M_{23}C_6$
4 (grey)	25.20	1.96	2.64	6.33	55.08	4.33	4.46	γ-Co

Interestingly, the TEM bright field image of the prepared bulk cobalt-based alloy (Figure 6) showed a large number of nano-twins in the γ-Co matrix. The thickness of twin lamellae varied between 10–60 nm.

The alloy had a high hardness of the 960 ± 9.2 HV5. Figure 7 shows the indentation morphology of the Vickers hardness test and the crack produced by the hardness indentation showing the fracture of $M_{12}C$ and $M_{23}C_6$-type carbide particles as well as the plastic deformation of γ-Co matrix, marked by arrows A, B, and C in the Figure 7b, respectively. Only a very short crack was found revealing that the prepared bulk alloy has a good toughness. According to the indentation methods for determining toughness, the fracture toughness K_{Ic} of the alloy was about 10.5 ± 0.46 MPa·m$^{1/2}$ calculated by the Equation (1) [15]:

$$K_{Ic} = \delta(E/H)^{1/2}(P/a^{3/2}),\tag{1}$$

where, δ is a geometrical factor, for a Vickers indentation $\delta = 0.016$; E is the Young's modulus, according to Ahmed's report [7], $E = 320$ GPa was selected in Equation (1); H is the hardness of the sample, $H = 960$ HV = 9.4 GPa; $2a$ is the crack size along the diagonal of the indentation, $2a = 115.2 ± 3.4$ μm; P is the load for Vickers indentation, $P = 49$ N.

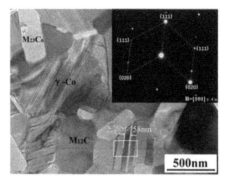

Figure 6. TEM bright field image of the sintered cobalt-based alloy showing a large number of nano-twins in the γ-Co matrix. Inlet is the SAED pattern for the marked area.

(**a**)   (**b**)

Figure 7. The indentation morphology of the Vickers indentation (**a**) and the crack generated by the indentation (**b**).

4. Discussion

The common cobalt-based alloy carbides are M_7C_3, $M_{23}C_6$, M_6C, MC, etc. Service or aging at elevated temperature causes a large amount of secondary carbides, such as M_6C and $M_{23}C_6$ [16]. In the present study, the prepared alloy had M_6C and $M_{23}C_6$-type carbides (Figure 4). The vanadium was mainly distributed in $M_{23}C_6$-type carbide in the prepared cobalt-based alloy, as shown in Table 1, instead of forming V-rich MC-type carbide. Even though vanadium is a strong MC-type carbide-forming or MX-type (M indicates metal elements, X indicates carbon or nitrogen) carbonitride-forming element, V-rich MC-type carbide is not found in the prepared bulk cobalt-based alloy with 5 wt. % V. However, MX-type precipitate is usually found in 9-12Cr-type martensitic/ferritic heat resistant steel with much less V content of 0.2 wt. % [17,18]. The microstructural characteristics of the prepared alloy is that the $M_{12}C$-type carbide particles and coarse $M_{23}C_6$-type carbide particles are distributed in the γ-Co matrix in which there are a large number of nano-twins, and fine $M_{23}C_6$-type carbide particles present within both the γ-Co matrix and $M_{12}C$-type carbide particles (Figure 3).

According to the results mentioned above, the microstructure formation mechanism of the prepared bulk cobalt-based alloy can be illustrated as shown in Figure 8. During the heating and hot pressed sintering process, the mechanically alloyed powders transform from an amorphous state with some nano-sized W particles to γ-Co supersaturated solid solution, then the $M_{12}C$-type and coarse $M_{23}C_6$-type carbides are formed as follows: $23(Cr, V) + 6C \rightarrow (Cr, V)_{23}C_6$ and $12(W, Cr, Co, V) + C \rightarrow (W, Cr, Co, V)_{12}C$ [19]. Finally, the fine $M_{23}C_6$-type carbide particles within both the γ-Co matrix and $M_{12}C$-type carbide particles are precipitated from the γ-Co matrix and $M_{12}C$-type carbide during the furnace cooling process after hot pressed sintering because their size is much smaller than that of the striplike $M_{23}C_6$ carbide. $M_{23}C_6$ carbide usually precipitates along grain boundaries during the cooling process in conventional alloys, such as austenitic steels and Ni-based superalloys. While the fine $M_{23}C_6$ carbide precipitates within γ-Co matrix in the present V-containing alloy, we think the reason might be that the $M_{23}C_6$ carbide contained a lot of V which has a larger atom size and lower diffusion coefficient than Cr resulting in nucleation of $M_{23}C_6$ within γ-Co matrix and growing up slowly.

The nominal composition of the alloy in atomic fraction was 35.8% Co, 40.1% Cr, 8.9% W, 5.5% Ni, 6.4% V, 3.2% C. From the STEM-EDS data as shown in Table 1, it can be seen that almost all W was distributed in $M_{12}C$, almost all V in $M_{23}C_6$ and the atomic fraction of Cr in $M_{23}C_6$ is about two times the atomic fraction of V. Based on the STEM-EDS data, the formation of $M_{12}C$ and $M_{23}C_6$ may consume about 6.1%C in atomic fraction, much more than the added 3.2% C. In fact, the carbon content in the prepared alloy was determined to be 1.9% in weight fraction, i.e., 9.8% in atomic fraction by a carbon and sulfur analyzer. The stainless-steel vial and stainless-steel balls were used to prepare the Co-based alloy powders in this work. According to the STEM-EDS results, only a small amount of Fe was indeed introduced into the sintered alloy, it is impossible that the carbon introduced from the stainless-steel vial and stainless-steel balls have much influence. The excess carbon may come from graphite mold during used for hot pressed sintering and causes an increase in amount of carbides.

The mechanism of nano-twins formation in the prepared cobalt-based alloy is not fully understood yet. Twins are common in metals with a FCC structure because of low stacking fault energy [20,21]. Twins are usually formed by sliding a single crystallographic dislocation on a continuous {111} plane driven by a Peach-Koehler force [22]. However, there is no report about the existence of large amounts of nano-twins in a cobalt-based alloy. From a thermodynamic point of view, the formation of twins decreases the total interfacial energy, because the excess energy for coherent twin boundaries (TB) is much smaller than that for conventional high angle grain boundaries (GB). Twins prefer to nucleate at GBs or triple junctions (TJ) to reduce the GB energies by means of the twinning-induced orientation change. Although an extra TB is formed, the sum of the interfacial energies (including GBs and TBs) will be reduced by twinning [23]. In the prepared alloy, the lattice constants of $M_{12}C$ and $M_{23}C_6$ carbides were 1.0922 nm and 1.0657 nm, respectively, about three times the γ-Co lattice constant (0.3552 nm) calculated using XRD data. Therefore, the interface between γ-Co and carbides are prone to form coherent interfaces, which causes a large lattice stress and increases the interfacial energy. In order to reduce the interfacial energies, a large number of nano-twins are formed in the γ-Co matrix.

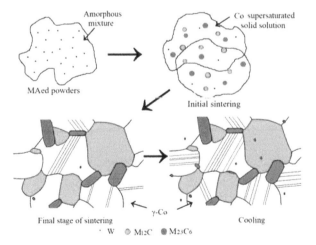

Figure 8. Schematic illustration of the microstructure evolution of cobalt-based alloy during hot pressing sintering and cooling.

The hardness of the prepared bulk cobalt-based alloy was up to 960 ± 9.2 HV5. Casas et al. [11] reported that the prepared ternary and quinary cobalt-based superalloys by field assisted sintering techniques have a hardness of about 650 and 900 HV, respectively. Ahmed [7] used Re-Hot Isostatic Pressing to prepare Stellite 20 alloy with a hardness of 650 HV. Compared with these reported results, the hardness of the prepared cobalt-based alloy in this work was increased significantly. It is reported that a Tribaloy T800 alloy coating has a hardness up to 1000 HV, however, the brittle nature of Laves phases causes a low fracture toughness and reduces the performance of T800 alloy in a wide range of applications where other properties such as certain ductility and fracture toughness are also needed [24]. The high hardness depends on the microstructure. A large amount of fine carbide dispersed uniformly in the prepared cobalt-based alloy, which served as a reinforcement agent. Carbides distributed at the γ-Co grain boundaries prevent slipping and migration of grain boundaries and inhibit grain growth. Carbides inside the γ-Co grains block dislocation movements to enhance the matrix. The W alloying element added in the cobalt based alloy was as high as 25%, which means that more W-containing $M_{12}C$ carbide in the prepared alloy can effectively improve the hardness, more than in a common cobalt based alloy [25]. In addition, many nano-twins are also found in the γ-Co matrix, which also play an important role in strengthening the matrix by blocking the dislocation motion [26,27], further enhancing the hardness. This is also the main difference in the reinforcement mechanism compared with the previously studied cobalt-based alloys [28]. Therefore, under the synergistic effect of solid solution strengthening, dispersion strengthening and nano-twins, the as-prepared cobalt-based alloy presents high hardness. Moreover, the matrix of the prepared Cobalt-based alloy is γ-Co with a FCC structure and has a fine grain structure. The crack propagation can be restrained by the plasticity of γ-Co matrix as shown in Figure 7 marked with arrow C. Therefore, the prepared cobalt-based alloy had not only high hardness but also good toughness, and a good wear-resistant property of the alloy can be expected.

5. Conclusions

In summary, a bulk V-containing cobalt-based alloy with high chromium and tungsten contents was prepared by mechanical alloying and hot pressed sintering using Co, Cr, W, Ni, V, and C pure element powders, the following can be concluded:

(1) All elements can be mixed uniformly while Co, Cr, and Ni elements are made into an amorphous state after 10h ball milling in a high energy ball miller.

(2) The microstructure of the prepared alloy was composed of γ-Co matrix with a large number of nano-twins and fine $M_{23}C_6$ and $M_{12}C$ carbide particles which were well-distributed in the alloy. The V element was mainly distributed in $M_{23}C_6$-type carbide and no V-rich MC-type carbide is found in the microstructure.

(3) The prepared alloy had a high hardness up to 960 ± 9.2 HV5 and good fracture toughness K_{Ic} of about 10.5 ± 0.46 MPa·m$^{1/2}$.

(4) The high hardness was mainly attributed to the synergistic effect of solid solution strengthening, dispersion strengthening, and the large number of nano-twins.

Author Contributions: Conceptualization, N.L.; methodology, N.L. and F.Y.; validation, N.L.; formal analysis, F.Y. and L.F.; writing—original draft preparation, N.L.; writing—review and editing, L.F.

Funding: This research was funded by the natural science foundation of Shandong province (Grant Number: ZR2016EMM01).

Acknowledgments: This work was supported by the natural science foundation of Shandong province (Grant Number: ZR2016EMM01). The authors are grateful for the assistance from Jinye Niu.

Conflicts of Interest: The authors declare no conflict of interest.

References

1. Petersson, A.; Ågren, J. Constitutive behaviour of WC–Co materials with different grain size sintered under load. *Acta Mater.* **2004**, *52*, 1847–1858. [CrossRef]

2. Mingard, K.P.; Roebuck, B.; Marshall, J.; Sweetman, G. Some aspects of the structure of cobalt and nickel binder phases in hardmetals. *Acta Mater.* **2011**, *59*, 2277–2290. [CrossRef]

3. Jiang, K.; Liu, R.; Chen, K.; Liang, M. Microstructure and tribological properties of solution-treated Tribaloy alloy. *Wear* **2013**, *307*, 22–27. [CrossRef]

4. Xu, W.; Liu, R.; Patnaik, P.C.; Yao, M.X.; Wu, X.J. Mechanical and tribological properties of newly developed Tribaloy alloys. *Mater. Sci. Eng. A* **2007**, *452–453*, 427–436. [CrossRef]

5. Sun, S.H.; Koizumi, Y.; Kurosu, S.; Li, Y.P.; Matsumoto, H.; Chiba, A. Build direction dependence of microstructure and high-temperature tensile property of Co–Cr–Mo alloy fabricated by electron beam melting. *Acta Mater.* **2014**, *64*, 154–168. [CrossRef]

6. Cordero, M.C.; Srinivasarao, B.; Campos, M.; Junceda, A.G.; Torralba, J.M. On the role of processing parameters in sintered new Co-based (W,Al) alloys. *J. Alloys Compd.* **2016**, *674*, 406–412. [CrossRef]

7. Ahmed, R.; Lovelock, H.L.V.; Davies, S.; Faisal, N.H. Influence of Re-HIPing on the structure–property relationships of cobalt-based alloys. *Tribol. Int.* **2013**, *57*, 8–21. [CrossRef]

8. You, X.H.; Wang, G.G.; Wang, J.; Xu, T.; Zhang, H.Y.; Wei, H. Effect of solid solution treatment on microstructure and mechanical properties of hot-press CoCrW alloys. *Acta Metall. Sin.* **2016**, *52*, 161–167.

9. Hou, J.; Dong, J.X.; Yao, Z.H.; Jiang, H.; Zhang, M.C. Influences of PPB, PPB affect zone, grain boundary and phase boundary on crack propagation path for a P/M superalloy FGH4096. *Mater. Sci. Eng. A* **2018**, *724*, 17–28. [CrossRef]

10. Zhang, L.; Qu, X.H.; He, X.B.; Din, R.; Qin, M.L.; Zhu, H.M. Hot deformation behavior of Co-base ODS alloys. *J. Alloys Compd.* **2012**, *512*, 39–46. [CrossRef]

11. Casasa, R.; Gálvez, F.; Campos, M. Microstructural development of powder metallurgy cobalt-based superalloys processed by field assisted sintering techniques (FAST). *Mater. Sci. Eng. A* **2018**, *724*, 461–468. [CrossRef]

12. Ren, F.Z.; Zhu, W.W.; Chu, K.J. Fabrication, tribological and corrosion behaviors of ultra-fine grained Co–28Cr–6Mo alloy for biomedical applications. *J. Mech. Behav. Biomed. Mater.* **2016**, *60*, 139–147. [CrossRef] [PubMed]

13. Berthod, P.; Khair, M. Thermodynamic and experimental study of cobalt-based alloys designed to contain TiC carbides. *Calphad* **2016**, *60*, 34–41. [CrossRef]

14. Burton, A.W.; Ong, K.; Rea, T.; Chan, I.Y. On the estimation of average crystallite size of zeolites from the Scherrer equation: A critical evaluation of its application to zeolites with one-dimensional pore systems. *Microp. Mesop. Mater.* **2009**, *117*, 75–90. [CrossRef]

15. Meyers, M.A.; Chawla, K.K. *Mechanical Behavior of Materials*; Cambridge University Press: Cambridge, UK, 2009; p. 549.

16. Yang, F.M.; Sun, X.F.; Zhang, W.; Kang, Y.P.; Guan, H.R.; Hu, Z.Q. Secondary M6C precipitation in K40S cobalt-base alloy. *Mater. Lett.* **2001**, *49*, 160–164. [CrossRef]

17. Zhang, C.; Cui, L.; Wang, D.P.; Liu, Y.C.; Liu, C.X.; Li, H.J. The heterogeneous microstructure of heat affect zone and its effect on creep resistance for friction stir joints on 9Cr–1.5W heat resistant steel. *Scrip. Mater.* **2019**, *158*, 6–10. [CrossRef]

18. Wang, H.; Yan, W.; Zwaag, S.; Shi, Q.Q.; Wang, W.; Yang, K.; Shan, Y.Y. On the 650 °C thermostability of 9–12Cr heat resistant steels containing different precipitates. *Acta Mater.* **2017**, *134*, 143–154. [CrossRef]

19. Jiang, W.H.; Yao, X.D.; Guan, H.R.; Hu, Z.Q.; Jiang, W.H. Secondary carbide precipitation in a directionally solified cobalt-base superalloy. *Metall. Mater. Trans. A* **1999**, *30*, 513–520. [CrossRef]

20. Szczerba, M.J.; Kopacz, S.; Szczerba, M.S. Experimental studies on detwinning of face-centered cubic deformation twins. *Acta Mater.* **2016**, *104*, 52–61. [CrossRef]

21. Mahajan, S. Critique of mechanisms of formation of deformation, annealing and growth twins: Face-centered cubic metals and alloys. *Scrip. Mater.* **2013**, *68*, 95–99. [CrossRef]

22. Gu, J.; Zhang, L.X.; Ni, S.; Song, M. Formation of large scaled zero-strain deformation twins in coarse-grained copper. *Scrip. Mater.* **2016**, *125*, 49–53. [CrossRef]

23. Lu, L.; Shen, Y.F.; Chen, X.H.; Qian, L.H.; Lu, K. Ultrahigh Strength and High Electrical Conductivity in Copper. *Science* **2004**, *304*, 422–425. [CrossRef]

24. Tobar, M.J.; Amado, J.M.; Álvarez, C.; García, A.; Varela, A.; Yáñez, A. Characteristics of Tribaloy T-800 and T-900 coatings on steel substrates by laser cladding. *Surf. Coat. Technol.* **2008**, *202*, 2297–2301. [CrossRef]

25. Lu, Y.J.; Wu, S.Q.; Gan, Y.L.; Li, J.L.; Zhao, C.Q.; Zhuo, D.X.; Lin, J.X. Investigation on the microstructure, mechanical property and corrosion behavior of the selective laser melted CoCrW alloy for dental application. *Mater. Sci. Eng. C* **2015**, *49*, 517–525. [CrossRef] [PubMed]

26. Liu, Y.Q.; Zhou, J.Q. The fatigue crack growth in hierarchically nano-twinned materials. *Eng. Fract. Mech.* **2018**, *204*, 63–71. [CrossRef]

27. Zhu, Y.T.; Liao, X.Z.; Wu, X.L. Deformation twinning in nanocrystalline materials. *Prog. Mater. Sci.* **2012**, *57*, 1–62. [CrossRef]

28. Corderoa, M.C.; Campos, M.; Freund, L.P.; Kolb, M.; Neumeier, S.; Göken, M.; Torralba, J.M. Microstructure and compression strength of Co-based superalloys hardened by γ' and carbide precipitation. *Mater. Sci. Eng. A* **2018**, *734*, 437–444. [CrossRef]

Article

Production of Ultrafine Grained Hardmetals by Electrical Resistance Sintering

Jesús Cintas [1], Raquel Astacio [1], Francisco G. Cuevas [2,*], Juan Manuel Montes [1],
Thomas Weissgaerber [3], Miguel Ángel Lagos [4], Yadir Torres [1] and José María Gallardo [1]

[1] Department of Materials Science and Engineering, Escuela Técnica Superior de Ingeniería,
Universidad de Sevilla, Camino de los Descubrimientos s/n, 41092 Sevilla, Spain; jcintas@us.es (J.C.);
rastacio@us.es (R.A.); jmontes@us.es (J.M.M.); ytorres@us.es (Y.T.); josemar@us.es (J.M.G.)

[2] Department of Chemical Engineering, Physical Chemistry and Materials Science, Escuela Técnica Superior
de Ingeniería, Universidad de Huelva, Campus El Carmen, Avda. Tres de Marzo s/n, 21071 Huelva, Spain

[3] Fraunhofer Institute for Manufacturing Technology and Advanced Materials, Winterbergstrasse 28,
01277 Dresden, Germany; Thomas.Weissgaerber@ifam-dd.fraunhofer.de

[4] Tecnalia Research & Innovation, Mikeletegi Pasealekua 2, 20009 San Sebastián, Spain;
miguel.lagos@tecnalia.com

* Correspondence: fgcuevas@dqcm.uhu.es; Tel.: +34-959217448

Received: 22 December 2018; Accepted: 28 January 2019; Published: 1 February 2019

Abstract: In this work, powders of cemented ultrafine WC-6 wt.% Co were consolidated. The feasibility of the medium frequency electrical resistance sintering (MF-ERS) technique were studied to prevent WC grain growth during consolidation. Porosity and hardness were measured at different zones of the MF-ERS compacts. The compacts showed a slight inhomogeneity in their properties across their section, but it was controlled by choosing suitable values of the processing parameters. The optimal values for the material studied were current intensities between 7 and 8 kA and sintering times between 600 and 800 ms. The main achievement using this consolidation method was that sintered compacts essentially maintained the initial WC grain size. This was attained to processing times of less than 2 s, and without the need for using protective atmospheres.

Keywords: electrical resistance sintering; hardmetal; ultrafine grain

1. Introduction

Conventional consolidation powder metallurgical (PM) techniques [1,2], mainly consisting of cold pressing and furnace sintering, are the most widely used, although the objective of finding a faster route has been a constant in researchers' mind.

New techniques are constantly emerging in an attempt to overcome the shortcomings of conventional processing. The direct use of electricity as a means to sinter powders has been suggested numerous times and with different approaches [3–11]. One of these techniques is electrical resistance sintering (ERS), in which heating is achieved by passing an electrical current through the powders.

The ERS process was already described in 1933 by Taylor [12] and later, in 1944, modified by Cremer [13], but its systematic study was not carried out until a few years later by Lenel [14]. Later, the ERS technique has incorporated technical variations of different importance [15,16]. Essentially, ERS involves the use of low voltage and high electrical current through a powder mass contained in an insulating die, while pressure is simultaneously applied. The medium frequency (about 1000 Hz) electrical resistance sintering (MF-ERS) technology has undergone an important evolution, making it possible to generate more heat for the same welding time.

The typical duration of the MF-ERS process is about one second. During this time, the applied current and pressure cause the densification of softened powders. This softening occurs by the temperature increase caused by the current passing through the powders, and the energy released by the Joule effect.

Among the advantages of this technique, as compared to the conventional PM route, the following should be considered: the use of relatively low pressures (around 100 MPa) to reach high densification rates, the need for very short processing times, and the possibility of sintering in air, without protective atmospheres.

WC, used in the productions of hardmetals or cemented carbides, has a high hardness and a low ductility, so that pieces of this material are usually made from powders by adding between 6% and 10% of Co as a binding agent [17]. WC–Co is mainly used in the production of tools for milling, drilling, and pressing/punching processes, although it is also used in jewelry or to make surgical instruments. Very good properties are attained by maintaining the size of WC grain size in the limit of 1 to 5 μm, although limiting the size to 0.5 μm allows achieving a unique combination of properties.

This paper details the production of hardmetal parts by electrical resistance sintering. The main aim of this work was to study the effect of current intensity and sintering time on the properties and grain size reached in different zones of the produced compacts.

2. Materials and Methods

The starting material was a commercially ultrafine WC-6 wt.% Co powder from Kyocera Unimerco (Sunds, Denmark). WC-6 wt.% Co powder was degassed (840 °C/0.75 h/N_2H_2) to avoid problems due to gases expulsion during processing, and pre-sintered (1100 °C/2 h/Ar) in order to increase its particle size and facilitate further processing. The carbon and oxygen content was 5.78 and 0.13 wt.%, respectively. Figure 1 shows the achieved granulated powder where the WC particle size was 262 ± 77 nm. Mean particle size of this degassed and pre-sintered powder (WC6Co) was 141 μm (Figure 1c), as measured by laser diffraction in a Mastersizer 2000 (Malvern Panalytical, Malvern, UK).

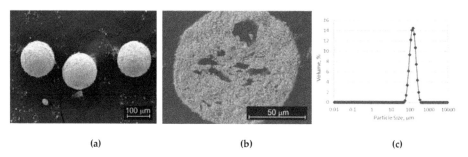

| (a) | (b) | (c) |

Figure 1. Degassed and pre-sintered WC-6 wt.% Co powder (WC6Co): Secondary electron SEM images of (**a**) the particles, (**b**) internal structure and (**c**) particle size distribution.

Compacts were prepared using a resistance welding machine (Beta 214 MF, Serra Soldadura, Barcelona, Spain), which was modified to implement the MF-ERS process. Figure 2a shows the scheme of the assembly used for MF-ERS, consisting of a 12 mm inner diameter ceramic tube (modified sodium zirconium phosphate-based ceramic, NZP) inserted in a metallic hoop. The powder mass (6.5 g in all experiences) was contained between two electrodes (thermal wafers and punches), all inside the ceramic tube. The temperature-resistant Cu electrodes (98.9% Cu, 1% Cr, 0.1% Zr) were in contact with heavy metal wafers (75.4% W, 24.6% Cu). These replaceable wafers were placed in direct contact with the powders to prevent electroerosion of the electrodes, powders sticking to the electrodes, and heat dissipation to the water-cooled electrodes due to their low thermal conductivity. In addition, to help the compacting process, the inner die wall was lubricated with a graphite–acetone suspension.

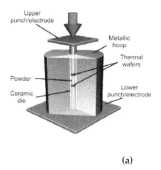 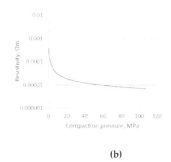

(a)   (b)

Figure 2. (a) Sketch of punches and die used in medium frequency electrical resistance sintering (MF-ERS) experiences, and (b) resistivity vs. compaction pressure of WC6Co powder.

The consolidation process consisted of three main stages: Cold pressing, sintering, and cooling. Compaction pressure, acting during the whole process, was 100 MPa for all the experiments. The cold-pressing and the cooling periods had a fixed duration of 1000 and 300 ms, respectively. The electrical current was only applied during the sintering stage. MF-ERS experiments were carried out with different current intensities and sintering times, always producing 12 mm diameter samples. Selected intensities were 6, 7, 8 and 9 kA, and heating times of 400, 600, 800 and 1000 ms were chosen. Intensities lower than 6 kA produced highly porous sintered samples. Intensities of 10 kA and above, combined with prolonged sintering times (1000 ms and longer), caused compacts welding to the wafers.

The previous description of the processing steps makes evident the importance of the relationship between the electrical resistivity and the compaction pressure, Figure 2b, because an adequate resistivity is required to allow the current passing at the time that causes the powders heating. Electrical resistance measurements were carried out by using a four-point probe with electrodes separated by 2 mm and a Kelvin bridge (micro-ohmmeter), by performing two measurements with inverted polarities to minimize the parasitic effects. Resistivity was determined from the measured resistance value. This powder showed a sharp drop in resistivity for low applied pressure values. The drop was lower as pressure increased. The resistivity values were between 3.76×10^{-4} and 6.87×10^{-6} Ωm in the range of 0 to 100 MPa.

Quantitative metallography on scanning electron microscopy (SEM) images (software Image Pro Plus 6, Media Cybernetics Inc., Rockville, MD, USA) was used to determine the porosity in specific regions of the compacts. The hardness of MF-ERS compacts was measured with a micro durometer Duramin-A300 (Struers GmbH, Willich, Germany), with the scale HV30, as recommended by the standard for hardmetals of this composition [18].

Samples were axially sectioned and subsequently prepared by appropriate grinding up to 400 grit SiC paper, and polishing on 6 and 3 μm diamond paste. Compact macrographs were taken with a D90 camera (Canon, Tokyo, Japan), and optical microscopy was performed with an EPIPHOT 200 microscope (Nikon, Tokyo, Japan). SEM studies of powders and compacts were carried out in a Dual Beam field emission gun scanning electron focused ion beam (FEGSEM-FIB) Auriga (Carl Zeiss, Oberkochen, Germany). In the case of sintered compacts, the same FEGSEM-FIB was required to resolve the exact morphology of these fine grained hardmetals. In order to improve the image quality, MF-ERS samples were, after being manually polished, ion etched into the microscope.

3. Results and Discussion

As compared to the relatively uniform porosity distribution in conventionally sintered compacts, MF-ERS compacts were characterized by a heterogeneous porosity distribution. Produced samples had a denser core than peripheral areas, as shown in Figure 3. This non-uniformity is the consequence of a heterogeneous temperature distribution during processing, as shown by the process simulation [19]. In MF-ERS, the heating is produced by the Joule effect in the internal part of the sample. The temperature in the exterior is lower due to the heat transfer to the punches and die (the former are refrigerated and the latter acts as a heat sink). Therefore, MF-ERS compacts densify more in the inner, usually presenting the external porous layer (the brighter area) shown in Figure 3b.

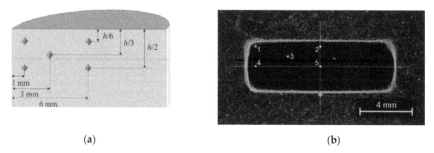

(a)   (b)

Figure 3. (a) Scheme and (b) metallographic section of a sintered sample showing the dot pattern where properties were studied.

In order to evaluate the homogeneity of the produced samples, properties at different zones of the specimen section have been studied. Taking into account the revolution symmetry of sintered compacts, a total of five zones distributed in a quadrant of an axial section of the compact were selected (Figure 3). In any case, measuring locations 1 to 5 were inside the zone limited by the porous outer layer surrounding the densified core of the specimen.

With the purpose of simplifying the graphical representation of the results, only the most representative zones (zones 1, 3 and 5) were shown. Zone 1 was chosen because it was located in the most extreme area of the compact, while zone 5 was in the center. Finally, zone 3 was at an intermediate distance from the previous ones.

Figure 4a shows the attained porosity, as a function of the current intensity, for 600 ms sintered compacts. As can be seen, the measured porosity values were always very low (less than 0.55 % and in general under 0.10 %). Even the porosity measured at zone 1, in the limit with the outer porous layer shown in Figure 3, was maintained at a very low value. Results reveal that the compact core (zone 5) was slightly more porous than the intermediate layer (zone 3). The reason for this was the air trapped inside the powder mass, which cannot be completely evacuated before closing the interconnected porosity, due to the very short sintering times. The porosity increases in zones 3 and 5 for the highest current intensity (9 kA) must be highlighted. The much quicker process under these circumstances accounts for this behavior.

Regarding the porosity evolution with sintering time (Figure 4b), a greater influence than with current intensity was observed. Increasing the sintering time increased the thermal transfer by Joule effect [20], causing the porosity to decrease as sintering time is extended. The same aforementioned phenomena of porosity increase for the most energetic conditions was observed for 1000 ms.

Therefore, it can be concluded that the best results, from the point of view of porosity, were achieved by sintering at not very high intensities (Figure 4a) and not very high heating times (Figure 4b), i.e., probably a good combination could result from 600 to 800 ms at 7 to 8 kA. These processing parameters also allowed a reduced outer porous layer, with a thickness lower than 100 μm. Mean density with the best conditions were therefore very near to that of commercial samples, around 14.75 g/cm^3 for the studied composition.

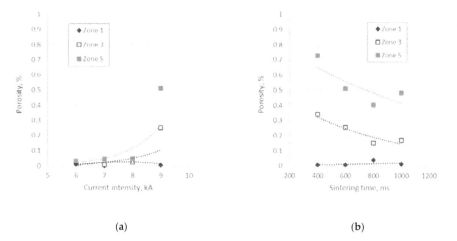

(a)   (b)

Figure 4. MF-ERS compacts porosity at zones 1, 3 and 5 as a function of (**a**) current intensity (experiences carried out at 600 ms), and (**b**) sintering time (experiences with 9 kA). Dotted lines are the trend lines of the different series.

In terms of hardness (Figure 5), most of the measured values are high, between 1800 and 2100 HV30. A typical value for commercial samples with this composition is around 1860 HV. The lowest values correspond to zones 3 and 5, according to the higher porosity at these zones, although possible different microstructural characteristics in both regions should also be considered.

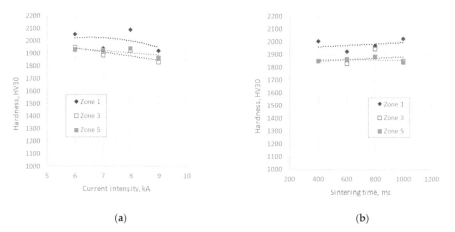

(a)   (b)

Figure 5. MF-ERS compacts hardness at zones 1, 3 and 5 as a function of (**a**) current intensity (experiences carried out with 600 ms), and (**b**) sintering time (experiences with 9 kA). Dotted lines are the trend lines of the different series.

The sintering conditions resulting in compacts with the best hardness values were between 600 and 800 ms, for intensities between 7 and 8 kA; that is, intervals coincident with those previously indicated for porosity.

Grain size is one of the most important factors in controlling materials properties. Mechanical strength, toughness, and hardness are important engineering properties that are strongly influenced by this parameter. For this reason, the tungsten carbide size distribution, along with Co interparticle free path, have been characterized in detail.

Measurement of carbide size was conducted according to the corresponding ISO standard [21]. As stated in the standard, a minimum of 200 grains of WC were measured to obtain a value as accurate as possible. This method was based on the average grain intercepts along a line across the material surface. In ultrafine grained hardmetals, as used in this study, the average grain size was so small that good quality images were difficult to obtain in conventional SEMs. However, it has been shown that a high resolution instrument which uses a field emission electron beam can provide acceptable images (Figure 6). The measurements of phase sizes were done after an ion etching (using the ion gun of the microscope) of the manually polished sample for improving the image quality.

(a)   (b)

Figure 6. Secondary electron field emission gun SEM (FEGSEM) images of WC6Co compacts sintered at 9 kA–600 ms. Images correspond to positions (**a**) 3 and (**b**) 5 of the axial section of the compact.

Figure 6 shows representative FEGSEM images of the microstructure of a 9 kA–600 ms MF-ERS compact in zones 3 and 5. Similar images have been used for the full characterization of the carbides after the MF-ERS processes carried out with different processing conditions.

The results of WC grain size measurements are shown in Table 1. Only representative values from zones 3 and 5, of samples sintered for 600 ms are shown. Mean WC grain size slightly varied with sintering current intensity, ranging between about 260 and 325 nm, although not clearly modifying carbide sizes in a particular trend. The mean value for zone 3 results was 289 nm, whereas for zone 5 it was 297 nm. Carbide size distributions are very flat, with differences in general below the standard deviation for these measurements, which as shown in Table 1 are below 50 nm. In addition, due to the smaller size of Co regions as compared to WC, the accuracy of the measurements is lower, resulting in mean values about 39 nm for zone 3 and 49 nm for zone 5.

Table 1. Effect of current intensity on WC mean grain size and Co mean free path at zones 3 and 5, measured along a line perpendicular to the pressing direction. Sintering time was 600 ms.

	Zone	Current Intensity, kA			
		6	7	8	9
WC Mean Size, nm	3	311 ± 45	267 ± 36	288 ± 31	289 ± 49
	5	258 ± 41	326 ± 25	287 ± 11	316 ± 28
Co Mean Free Path, nm	3	34 ± 4	37 ± 6	46 ± 9	38 ± 5
	5	49 ± 9	40 ± 8	53 ± 8	53 ± 7

Regarding the effect of sintering time, measurements on compacts sintered with a fixed current of 9 kA have been carried out (Table 2). WC mean size ranged between 273 and 327, with the Co mean free path between 37 and 60 nm for sintering times between 400 and 1000 ms. Again, there is not a clear effect of sintering time on microstructural features. Differences between both measuring zones and/or different sintering times were below the standard deviations for these measurements.

Table 2. Effect of sintering time on WC mean grain size and Co mean free path at zones 3 and 5, measured along a line perpendicular to the pressing direction. All samples were sintered at 9 kA.

	Zone	Sintering Time, ms			
		400	600	800	1000
WC Mean Size, nm	3	321 ± 52	289 ± 49	327 ± 49	309 ± 57
	5	273 ± 25	316 ± 28	301 ± 39	287 ± 20
Co Mean Free Path, nm	3	37 ± 4	38 ± 5	41 ± 5	52 ± 9
	5	60 ± 11	53 ± 7	58 ± 10	51 ± 7

In general, and comparing all the measured values, zone 5 showed slightly bigger grain sizes and Co mean free paths. As previously explained, the highest temperatures during MF-ERS processing were reached at zone 5, which could be consistent with the very slight increase in grain size observed.

It is also interesting to compare the WC grain size distributions in regions 3 and 5 of any particular sample. Figure 7 shows these values for the 7 KA–600 ms sintered compact. A higher percentage of small grains were measured at zone 3, although the minimum and maximum grain sizes were not so different. This was again in agreement with the highest temperature being reached at the core of the specimen.

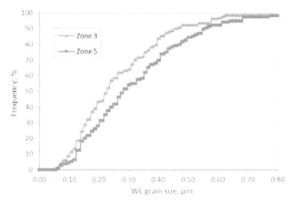

Figure 7. WC grain size distribution at zones 3 and 5 of compact sintered at 7 kA during 600 ms.

Regarding the effect on the WC grain size of the starting powder (262 ± 77 nm), it can be concluded that whichever the MF-ERS conditions, the WC grain size does not significantly grow during sintering. This is particularly important because using conventional hardmetals sintering methods, the WC grain size increased very quickly from the first few minutes of sintering [22]. In practice, to maintain such fine microstructures, grain growth inhibitors such as Cr_3C_2 or VC must be added in the material composition [23]. The proposed method of MF-ERS allows the ultrafine grain size of the WC powder to be maintained without using these additives. The high speed of the method is the key. This also brings another important aspect to highlight: there is no need to use protective atmospheres during sintering.

Finally, although out of the scope of this manuscript to be treated in detail, it is worth noting the toughness values reached in these materials. Palmqvist cracks induced from the corners of the Vickers indentation were related to the fracture toughness of the WC–Co [24]. Values show a certain anisotropy that can be eliminated through a heat treatment at 800 °C, reaching, for instance after processing at 7 kA and 800 ms, a mean value around 8.5 $MPa·m^{1/2}$.

4. Conclusions

In this work, ultrafine WC6Co powder was consolidated by MF-ERS. Results indicated that produced compacts were not completely homogeneous, with a slight variation of properties depending on the zone of the specimen under consideration. Only a porous layer as thin as 100 μm was obtained in the outer surface of sintered samples.

Thus, for certain processing conditions (8 kA and 600 ms), porosity can be limited to values below 0.1%, regardless of the measuring zone of the cross section of the sample.

The hardness of sintered compacts was high, reaching for 8 kA and 600 ms values higher than 1900 HV30 at any zone of the sample.

It must be highlighted that the MF-ERS method has been proved perfectly suitable for producing, in less than two seconds, ultrafine hardmetals compacts with WC grain size in the order of the 300 nm, without the need for using a protective atmosphere.

Author Contributions: Conceptualization, J.M.G. and J.M.M.; methodology, J.C., F.G.C. and M.A.L.; validation, R.A., T.W. and Y.T.; writing—original draft preparation, J.C. and F.G.C.; writing—review and editing, all authors.

Funding: The authors are grateful to the EU for funding this research within the framework of the EU 7th Framework Programme, grant number FoF.NMP.2013-10 608729, Energy Efficient Process of Engineering Materials, EFFIPRO Project.

Acknowledgments: The authors thank the Microscopy Central Service (CITIUS, University of Seville) for the use of their facilities.

Conflicts of Interest: The authors declare no conflict of interest. The funders had no role in the design of the study, in the collection, analyses, or interpretation of data, in the writing of the manuscript, or in the decision to publish the results.

References

1. Cintas, J.; Montes, J.M.; Cuevas, F.G.; Gallardo, J.M. Influence of PCA content on mechanical properties of sintered MA aluminium. *Mater. Sci. Forum* **2006**, *514–516*, 1279–1283. [CrossRef]
2. Cintas, J.; Montes, J.M.; Cuevas, F.G.; Herrera, E.J. Influence of milling media on the microstructure and mechanical properties of mechanically milled and sintered aluminium. *J. Mater. Sci.* **2005**, *40*, 3911–3915. [CrossRef]
3. Grasso, S.; Sakka, Y.; Maizza, G. Electric current activated/assisted sintering (ECAS): A review of patents 1906–2008. *Sci. Technol. Adv. Mater.* **2009**, *10*, 1–24. [CrossRef] [PubMed]
4. Okazaki, K. Electro-discharge consolidation of particulate materials. *Rev. Part. Mater.* **1994**, *2*, 215–269.
5. Raichenko, A.I.; Chernikova, E.S. A mathematical model of electric heating of the porous medium using current-supplying electrode/punches. *Sov. Powder Metall. Met. Ceram.* **1989**, *28*, 365–371. [CrossRef]
6. Burenkov, G.L.; Raichenko, A.I.; Suraeva, A.M. Macroscopic mechanism of formation of interparticle contact in electric current sintering of powders. *Sov. Powder Metall. Met. Ceram.* **1989**, *28*, 186–191. [CrossRef]
7. Groza, J.R.; Zavaliangos, A. Sintering activation by external electrical field. *Mater. Sci. Eng. A* **2000**, *287*, 171–177. [CrossRef]
8. Wang, C.; Cheng, L.; Zhao, Z. FEM analysis of the temperature and stress distribution in spark plasma sintering: Modelling and experimental validation. *Comput. Mater. Sci.* **2010**, *49*, 351–362. [CrossRef]
9. Biesuz, M.; Pinter, L.; Saunders, T.; Reece, M.; Binner, J.; Sglavo, V.M.; Grasso, S. Investigation of electrochemical, optical and thermal effects during flash sintering of 8YSZ. *Materials* **2018**, *11*, 1214. [CrossRef] [PubMed]
10. Biesuz, M.; Dong, J.; Fu, S.; Liu, Y.; Zhang, H.; Zhu, D.; Hu, C.; Grasso, S. Thermally-insulated flash sintering. *Scr. Mater.* **2019**, *162*, 99–102. [CrossRef]
11. Biesuz, M.; Sglavo, V.M. Flash sintering of ceramics. *J. Eur. Ceram. Soc.* **2019**, *39*, 115–143. [CrossRef]
12. Taylor, G.F. Apparatus for Making Hardmetal Compositions. U.S. Patent 1,896,854A, 7 February 1933.
13. Cremer, G.D. Powder Metallurgy. U.S. Patent 2,355,954A, 15 August 1944.
14. Lenel, F.V. Resistance sintering under pressure. *Trans. AIME* **1955**, *7*, 158–167. [CrossRef]
15. Hara, Z.; Akechi, K. Electrical resistance sintering of titanium metal, alloys and composites. In *Titanium'80, Science and Technology, Proceedings of the 4th International Conference on Ti, Kyoto, Japan, 19–22 May 1980*; Kimura, H., Izumi, O., Eds.; The Metallurgical Society of AIME: New York, NY, USA, 1980; pp. 2265–2274.
16. Montes, J.M.; Rodríguez, J.A.; Cuevas, F.G.; Cintas, J. Consolidation by electrical resistance sintering of Ti powder. *J. Mater. Sci.* **2011**, *46*, 5197–5207. [CrossRef]

17. Pötschke, J.; Säuberlich, T.; Vornberger, A.; Meese-Marktscheffel, J.A. Solid state sintered nanoscaled hardmetals and their properties. *Int. J. Refract. Met. Hard Mater.* **2018**, *72*, 45–50. [CrossRef]

18. *Hardmetals: Vickers Hardness Test*; ISO 3878; ISO: Geneva, Switzerland, 1983.

19. Montes, J.M.; Cuevas, F.G.; Cintas, J.; Urban, P. A One-Dimensional Model of the Electrical Resistance Sintering Process. *Metall. Mater. Trans. A* **2015**, *46*, 963–980. [CrossRef]

20. Montes, J.M.; Cintas, J.; Cuevas, F.G.; Rodriguez, J.A. Electrical resistance sintering of M.A. Al-5AlN powders. *Mater. Sci. Forum* **2006**, *514–516*, 1225–1229. [CrossRef]

21. Hardmetals: Metallographic Determination of Microstructure. *Part 2: Measurement of WC Grain Size*; ISO 4499-2; ISO: Geneva, Switzerland, 2008.

22. Mannesson, K.; Elfwing, M.; Kusoffsky, A.; Norgren, S.; Ågren, J. Analysis of WC grain growth during sintering using electron backscatter diffraction and image analysis. *Int. J. Refract. Met. Hard Mater.* **2008**, *26*, 449–455. [CrossRef]

23. Pötschke, J.; Richter, V.; Gestrich, T.; Säuberlich, T.; Meese-Marktscheffel, J.A. Grain growth inhibition in ultrafine hardmetals. *Int. J. Refract. Met. Hard Mater.* **2017**, *66*, 95–104. [CrossRef]

24. Ponton, C.B.; Rawlings, R.D. Vickers indentation fracture toughness test, part 1: Review of literature and formulation of standardised indentation toughness equations. *Mater. Sci. Technol.* **1989**, *5*, 865–872. [CrossRef]

MDPI

St. Alban-Anlage 66

4052 Basel

Switzerland

Tel. +41 61 683 77 34

Fax +41 61 302 89 18

www.mdpi.com

Metals Editorial Office

E-mail: metals@mdpi.com

www.mdpi.com/journal/metals